Matter, Motion, and Machines

AGS

by
Robert H. Marshall
Allen Rosskopf

AGS®

American Guidance Service, Inc.
4201 Woodland Road
Circle Pines, MN 55014-1796
1-800-328-2560

Experiences in Science

Printed in the United States of America

ISBN 0–7854–0971–8 (Previously ISBN 0–88671–535–0)

Order Number: 90892

A 0 9 8 7 6

Contents

Introduction

What is Physical Science?

Guide Question: What is physical science?

Vocabulary:
analyze	energy	observe
classify	law	principle
data	matter	theory

Who are physical scientists? Mainly, they are scientists who study matter and energy. Some study how energy is contained in matter. Some predict how matter will react under certain conditions. Others develop theories about how energy affects matter. Their work helps others make better use of energy.

Matter is everything that we can see, feel, or measure. All objects, big and small, are made up of matter. **Energy** can be thought of as the power to change or move matter. All matter has energy because it is made up of atoms that are constantly moving. When energy is used, motion results. For example, your hand is made of matter. It can be a powerful tool, but only if it has enough energy to do work. Energy is used any time work is done. Your hand uses the heat energy that you get from food. Other kinds of energy are electrical, chemical, and nuclear.

Physical scientists look at many kinds of matter. In other words, they look closely at, or **observe,** everything around them. Then they record what they have observed. These records are called **data.** Data may include a simple description of something or a list of measurements. Once the facts are collected, the scientists group the data in different ways. For example, energy is grouped, or **classified,** into types.

Scientists also **analyze,** or examine, the data to discover rules about the physical world. Their ideas about relationships in the physical world are called **theories.** Once theories are developed, they are tested over and over again by many different scientists. Theories that have been tested many times and have proved to be accurate may be accepted as **laws** or **principles** of science.

In this book, you will learn about the two major categories of physical science. They are

| **Chemistry** | the study of structure and energy in matter |
| **Physics** | the study of motion, force, and energy |

Looking Back—Getting the Point

Complete as many of the exercises as you can without referring back to what you have just read. See what you can answer without checking. However, if necessary, look back at the previous page to finish the exercises.

A Write the vocabulary word that matches each definition.

1. examine _____

2. the power to change or move matter _____

3. something that can be seen or felt_____

4. look closely at_____

5. group according to types_____

B Use a vocabulary word to fill in each of the blanks.

1. A computer is useful in physical science because it can hold a large amount of

_____.

2. An unproven scientific hunch or opinion is called a _____.

3. Once a theory is accepted, it may become a law or _____.

C Answer these questions.

1. What are the two major fields of physical science? _____

_____

2. What are three things that physical scientists do?

_____

_____

_____

3. What is the difference between a theory and a law or principle? _____

_____

4. What are examples of three types of energy? _____

_____

The Five Senses

Guide Question: How do scientists use their senses?

Vocabulary: comparison   properties

When scientists look at things, they look for **properties,** or individual details. A scientist is not satisfied to say that a ball is round. A scientist wants to describe the ball completely, to record all of its properties.

Scientists record their observations in two ways. Scientists may list measurements (quantitative), or they may create descriptions (qualitative) of the properties of an object. Measurements often require the use of special tools.

Descriptions sometimes make use of **comparisons** between things. When you compare things, you tell how they are alike or different. Simple description is important to the physical scientist because it allows quick identification of properties. For instance, the quickest way to identify salt in water is to taste it. Description also depends on the five senses:

- Hearing (sound)
- Sight (color, size, shape)
- Taste (salty, bitter, sour, sweet)
- Touch (texture, softness, or hardness)
- Smell (sweet, smoky, flowery)

A Write your answer to each activity.

1. Name something that you can identify by its *sound*. _____

2. Name something that you can identify by its *color*. _____

3. Name something that you can identify by its *shape*. _____

4. Name something that you can identify by its *taste*. _____

5. Name something that you can identify by its *feel*. _____

6. Name something that you can identify by its *smell*. _____

That was not easy, was it? You probably realize that you could use more than one sense to identify each object you listed. Now go back to the previous page. Next to each object, name at least one other sense that you could use to identify it.

B Now try it another way. For each object, list two senses that you could use to identify the object if it were given to you.

1. an orange _____

2. a pencil _____

3. a puppy _____

4. a stick of cinnamon _____

5. a clock _____

6. a lamp that is lit _____

7. a guitar _____

8. a bell _____

C Things that have similar properties require even more thought to identify. Think about the pairs of objects listed below and explain how they are different.

1. a bumblebee and a lawn mower _____

_____

_____

2. a rose and a tulip _____

_____

_____

3. a pencil and a pen _____

_____

_____

4. a baseball and a softball _____

_____

_____

5. a cup and a bowl _____

_____

Another method of description is to compare the properties of one less familiar object to the properties of a more familiar object. For instance, if you know what almonds smell like, you would be able to identify the smell of the deadly poison cyanide. You make these kinds of observations every day. These comparisons use the words *like* or *as.* For example, Cyanide smells *like* almonds.

D Complete the following comparisons.

1. The metal glitters like _____

   _____

2. The liquid smelled as sour as _____

   _____

3. The powder was as yellow as _____

   _____

4. The light was as bright as _____

   _____

5. The motor was as loud as _____

   _____

When you describe an object, use all of your senses and take time to identify as many properties as you can—as well as you can. This is part of the job of the physical scientist.

Many descriptions depend on comparisons to other sense experiences. You make these kinds of observations every day.

E Choose an object you can observe right now. List as many properties of the object as you can. Then write a description of it. Try to include one comparison that uses the words *like* or *as.*

_____

_____

_____

_____

_____

The Metric System

Guide Question: What is the metric system?
Vocabulary: distance   meter   metric system

Description is one way scientists record data. The second type of data recording is measurement. To measure means to compare the size of an object with the size of another known object. These known objects are called units. The **metric system** of measurement for length is based on a unit called a meter.

The standard **meter** is a little longer than a yardstick. It is actually 1.09 yards long. For shorter **distances**, other units can be chosen that are smaller than a meter. The most common smaller units are shown in the following table.

1 Unit	Part of one meter	Also equal to
1 decimeter	$\frac{1}{10}$ of a meter	10 centimeters
1 centimeter	$\frac{1}{100}$ of a meter	10 millimeters
1 millimeter	$\frac{1}{1,000}$ of a meter	

Notice that each of the units is one-tenth of the unit above it. A decimeter is $\frac{1}{10}$ of a meter. A centimeter is $\frac{1}{10}$ of a decimeter or $\frac{1}{10} \times \frac{1}{10} = \frac{1}{100}$ of a meter. A millimeter is $\frac{1}{10}$ of a centimeter or $\frac{1}{10} \times \frac{1}{10} \times \frac{1}{10} = \frac{1}{1,000}$ of a meter. There are units smaller than a millimeter, but they will not be used in this book.

Meter stick

Because of this relationship between units, it is easy to change from one to another. When changing larger units into smaller units, multiply by a power of 10. When changing smaller units into larger units, divide by a power of 10.

Generally, scientists prefer the metric system to the English system because it is easier to multiply and divide in the metric system. For example, in order to convert miles to inches, you must find the number of inches in a mile.

Here is the way to convert three miles into inches:

3 miles = 3 x 5,280 (feet in a mile) x 12 (inches in a foot)

3 miles = 15,840 feet x 12 (inches in a foot)

3 miles = 190,080 inches

In the metric system, you might be converting kilometers into centimeters. Conversion would look like this:

3 kilometers = 3 x 1,000 (meters in a kilometer) x 100 (centimeters in a meter)

3 kilometers = 3,000 x 100 = 300,000 centimeters

How many centimeters are there in 6 kilometers? Can you multiply it in your head? Which one would you rather figure out? When converting units in the metric system, use this chart to help remember the unit equivalents.

Metric Equivalents		
1 kilometer	=	1,000 meters
1 meter	=	10 decimeters
1 meter	=	100 centimeters
1 meter	=	1,000 millimeters

Example 1: Change 2 meters into decimeters.
Meters are larger than decimeters, so multiply by 10:
2 (meters) x 10 (decimeters per meter) = 20 decimeters

Example 2: Change 4 meters into centimeters.
Meters are larger than centimeters, so multiply by 100:
4 (meters) x 100 (centimeters per meter) = 400 centimeters

Example 3: Change 20 millimeters into centimeters.
Millimeters are smaller than centimeters, so divide by 10:
20 (millimeters) ÷ 10 (millimeters per centimeter) = 2 centimeters

Example 4: Change 40 centimeters into meters.
Centimeters are smaller than meters, so divide by 100:
40 (centimeters) ÷ 100 (centimeters per meter) = .4 meter

A Change each of the following measurements into millimeters.

1. 8 meters = _____ millimeters

2. 6 centimeters = _____ millimeters

3. 3 decimeters = _____ millimeters

4. 5 centimeters = _____ millimeters

5. 3.2 centimeters = _____ millimeters

B Change each of the following measurements into meters.

1. 350 millimeters = _____ meters

2. 120 centimeters = _____ meters

3. 15 decimeters = _____ meters

4. 89 centimeters = _____ meters

5. 9.8 decimeters = _____ meters

C Choose the unit best suited for measuring the following.

1. the thickness of your pencil _____

2. the distance to the moon _____

3. the length of your classroom _____

4. the cover of this book _____

5. the distance to the nearest city _____

6. a person's height _____

7. the length of your shoe_____

8. the waist size of your pants _____

D Underline the larger measurement.

1. 5 kilometers or 50,000 meters

2. 5 kilometers or 2,500 meters

3. 5 meters or 450 centimeters

4. 1 centimeter or 3 millimeters

5. 35 centimeters or 1 meter

Units of Measurement

Guide Question: How do scientists use derived units?

Vocabulary: volume

In the previous lesson, you learned that scientists use the metric system for their measurements. The metric system is based on the meter, a unit of length. Other units can be derived from the unit of length.

Volume is the amount of space that an object takes up. The unit of volume in the metric system is the liter. A liter is the volume of a cube that is one decimeter on each side. A volume of one cubic decimeter is the same as one liter.

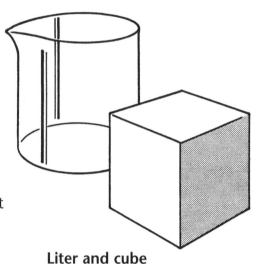

Liter and cube

For objects that have a regular shape, like a cube or a rectangular prism, you can use a formula to calculate its volume.

volume of a cube = side x side x side

volume of a rectangular prism = length x width x height

Example: Find the volume of a cube that is 24 decimeters on each side.

volume = 2 dm x 2 dm x 2 dm

volume = 8 cubic dm = 8 l

Cube of water

The gram is the unit of mass in the metric system. Mass tells how much matter an object contains. A gram is the mass of a cube of water that is one centimeter on each side. Mass is measured using a balance scale. You will learn how to use the scale in a later lesson.

The following tables show how each of the units of the metric system are related to each other. Study each of them, and then complete the problems.

Length			Mass		
1 kilometer	=	1,000 meters	1 kilogram	=	1,000 grams
1 meter	=	100 centimeters	1 gram	=	100 centigrams
1 centimeter	=	10 millimeters	1 centigram	=	10 milligrams
1 meter	=	1,000 millimeters	1 gram	=	1,000 milligrams

Volume		
1 kiloliter	=	1,000 liters
1 liter	=	100 centiliters
1 centiliter	=	10 milliliters
1 liter	=	1,000 milliliters

A Convert the following measurements into the units shown.

1. 10 centimeters = _____ millimeters

2. 2 grams = _____ centigrams

3. 5 liters = _____ milliliters

4. 30 milliliters _____ centiliters

5. 50 kilograms = _____ grams

B Underline the measurement that is larger.

1. 8 millimeters or 1 centimeter

2. 1 liter or 1,001 milliliters

3. 5 centigrams or 40 milligrams

4. 800 grams or 1 kilogram

5. 18 centimeters or 190 millimeters

6. 4 liters or 200 centiliters

C Use the formulas for volume of a cube and volume of a rectangular prism to calculate these volumes.

1. Find the volume of a cube that is 4 decimeters on each side. Express your answer in both cubic decimeters and liters. _____ cubic decimeters   _____ liters

2. Find the volume of a rectangular prism that has a length of 3 centimeters, a width of 2 centimeters, and a height of 4 centimeters. Express your answer in cubic centimeters.

    _____ cubic centimeters

Rulers, Scales, and Graduated Cylinders

Guide Question: What basic laboratory tools are used for measurement?

Vocabulary: balance scale   meter stick
                 graduated cylinder   spring scale

A science laboratory is arranged with instruments that scientists need to measure the world around them. Each tool is designed to measure certain properties. The scientist must select the tool that will do the job best.

Measuring Distance

The **meter stick** is used to measure distances. Most meter sticks are made from wood. They can also be made from steel or some other metal. Meter sticks made from metal usually have a better edge on them because they do not wear down from constant use.

Meter sticks are one meter in length. They are subdivided into centimeters and millimeters. Often only the centimeters are numbered. Each millimeter is not numbered because there is not enough space to do so.

The meter is divided into one hundred centimeters, and each centimeter is divided into 10 millimeters. A meter, then, is equal to 100 centimeters or 1,000 millimeters.

Standard ruler

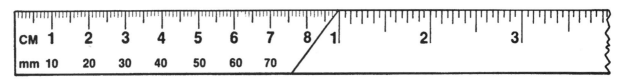

Centimeters and Millimeters   **Inches**

A ruler is also used for measuring distances. It is sometimes more convenient than a meter stick because it is shorter. Most rulers are made with two scales. On one side is a scale in centimeters and millimeters. The other side shows inches, which are broken down into halves, quarters, eighths, and sometimes sixteenths. Most rulers are one foot long (twelve inches).

Avoid using the edge of the ruler as the starting point for measuring distances. Often the edge is rounded or damaged and the measurement will be off slightly. Instead, choose one of the major lines, such as the one-inch or one-centimeter mark. Then find the end point of the object being measured and subtract one inch or one centimeter from the total length shown on the ruler. See the ruler on page 15.

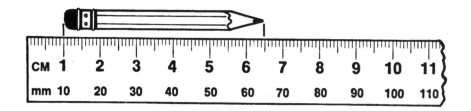

CM	1	2	3	4	5	6	7	8	9	10	11
mm	10	20	30	40	50	60	70	80	90	100	110

A Measure the lines next to each number. Use both a meter stick and a ruler. Round your answers to the nearest $\frac{1}{2}$ in centimeters and $\frac{1}{4}$ in inches. Express your answers as decimals. (Examples: 7.5 centimeters for $7\frac{1}{2}$ centimeters; 2.75 inches for $2\frac{3}{4}$ inches)

1. _____

_____ centimeters   _____ inches

2. _____

_____ centimeters   _____ inches

3. _____

_____ centimeters   _____ inches

4. _____

_____ centimeters   _____ inches

Measuring Weight

A scientist measures weight with either a **balance scale** or a **spring scale.** The balance scale is usually a more accurate tool than the spring scale. This is true because the spring in a spring scale may lose some of its tension with use.

You can see a spring scale in the grocery store. Most vegetables and fruits are located near a hanging scale that is used to measure the weight of the produce.

Some balance scales look like seesaws with two pans, one on either side of a center point. The object to be weighed is placed in one pan and known weights are added to the other pan until the two sides balance.

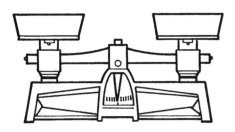

Laboratory balance scale

Measuring Volume

To measure volume means to measure the amount of space that an object occupies. If an object has a regular shape such as a cube or a ball, the volume can be calculated using a formula. For example, the volume of a cube is calculated by multiplying the measurements of the length, the width, and the height. The volume of a cube that is 2 centimeters on each side would be 2 centimeters x 2 centimeters x 2 centimeters, or 8 cubic centimeters.

The volume of liquid is measured by pouring it into a **graduated cylinder,** or a beaker, that is marked with a scale. In the metric system, the units are marked as cubic centimeters or milliliters. One milliliter is the same as one cubic centimeter.

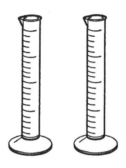

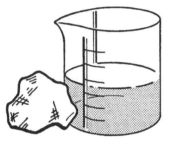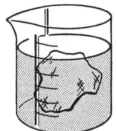

The volume of irregular objects (a rock, for instance) can be measured by the water displacement method. In this method, a graduated cylinder is filled with water to a specific level. Then the object is placed in the cylinder. The water level will rise to a new point. The volume of the object is equal to the change in water level.

Measuring Other Properties

Scientists measure many other properties, such as temperature, wind speed, barometric pressure, and electrical voltages. The chart below lists some of the instruments scientists use and the properties they measure.

Instrument	Property Measured
thermometer	temperature
barometer	air pressure
hygrometer	humidity
anemometer	wind speed
voltmeter	voltage
calorimeter	heat
seismograph	earthquake waves
speedometer	speed

Laboratory Exercise—Measure Density

Density is calculated by dividing an object's weight by its volume. The density of a substance is always the same, regardless of how much of that substance exists. For example, a piece of paper has a certain weight. If you put 100 sheets of paper together, they will weigh 100 times the weight of a single piece because the density of paper remains the same. Density is written in the form of grams per cubic centimeter (g/cc) or pounds per cubic foot (lbs./cu.ft.).

Materials

scale (either balance or spring)   small pebble or stone
graduated cylinder   water

Procedure

1. Use your scale to measure the weight of your stone.
2. Record the weight in the data table below.
3. Fill the graduated cylinder with enough water to cover the pebble.
4. Record this water level.
5. Place the pebble in the cylinder with the water and record the new water level.
6. Subtract the old water level from the new water level.
7. Record this number as the volume in the data table.
8. Divide the weight of the pebble by the volume of the pebble.
9. Record this number as the density of the pebble.

Weight	Water level 1	Water level 2	Volume	Density

B Answer these questions.

1. Find the density of an object with a weight of 18 grams if it has a volume of

   3 cubic centimeters. _____ g/cc

2. Find the density of a rock weighing 88 grams. The graduated cylinder is filled to a level of 25 cubic centimeters. The water level rises to a level of 36 cubic centimeters when the rock is placed in the cylinder. Record your findings in the data table below.

Weight	Water level 1	Water level 2	Volume	Density

3. What is the density of an object that has a weight of 64 grams and a volume of 8 cubic centimeters? _____

4. Which object has the greater density, a rock weighing 5 pounds with a volume of 2 cubic feet or a rock weighing 10 pounds with a volume of 3 cubic feet? _____

5. Gold has a density of 19.3 grams per cubic centimeter. A scientist has been given an object that appears to be gold. It weighs 220 grams and has a volume of 16 cubic centimeters. Is it gold? Why or why not?

_____

_____

_____

6. Fill in the missing spaces in the following data table.

Weight	Water level 1	Water level 2	Volume	Density
10 g	20cc	30cc		1g/cc
	15cc		5cc	2g/cc
	25cc	32cc		6g/cc
28g		16cc	4cc	
	31cc		8cc	8g/cc

Thermometers

Guide Question: How do scientists use thermometers?
Vocabulary: Celsius scale   degree   Fahrenheit scale   thermometer

Scientists use an instrument called a **thermometer** to measure the temperature of objects. Temperature measures the average motion of particles in matter. Faster-moving particles create higher temperatures. There are two scales that are widely used to measure temperature. On the **Fahrenheit scale,** the temperature of boiling water is 212 **degrees.** On this scale, the average body temperature of human beings is 98.6 degrees. The Fahrenheit scale is used mostly in the United States. The second scale is part of the metric system. It is called the **Celsius scale.** On this scale, water freezes at 0 degrees and boils at 100 degrees. In your science work, you will use the Celsius thermometer.

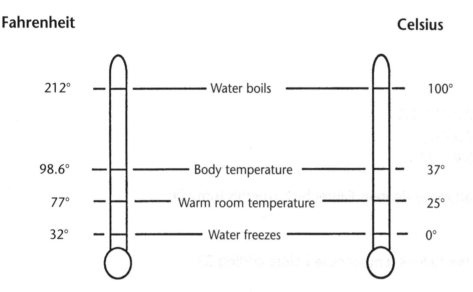

A thermometer, either Fahrenheit or Celsius, is marked with lines that show temperature in degrees. This symbol, °, is used to indicate degrees. Because the degree lines are close together, only certain numbers are shown on the thermometer. Two common methods of numbering the degrees are by *twos (92, 94, 96)* and by *fives (90, 95, 100).*

Because both of the temperature scales are in use in the United States, it may be necessary for you to change a temperature from Celsius to Fahrenheit or from Fahrenheit to Celsius. A formula can help you make this change.

To change Fahrenheit temperatures to degrees Celsius, use this formula:

$$C = 5/9 \times (F-32)$$

C is the Celsius temperature.

F is the Fahrenheit temperature.

When using this formula, first subtract 32 from the Fahrenheit temperature and then multiply that number by 5/9. Follow these steps:

Example 1: Change 41 degrees Fahrenheit to degrees Celsius.

  Step 1: C = 5/9 x (F–32)

  Step 2: C = 5/9 x (41–32)

  Step 3: C = 5/9 x (9)

  Step 4: C = 5°

Example 2: Change 72 degrees Fahrenheit to degrees Celsius.

  Step 1: C = 5/9 x (F–32)

  Step 2: C = 5/9 x (72–32)

  Step 3: C = 5/9 x (40)

  Step 4: C= 200/9 = 22.2°

To change Celsius temperatures to degrees Fahrenheit, use this formula:

F = (9/5 x C) + 32

Note: Be sure to multiply the Celsius temperature before adding 32.

Example 3: Change 15 degrees Celsius to degrees Fahrenheit.

  Step 1: F = (9/5 x C) + 32

  Step 2: F = (9/5 x 15/1) + 32

  Step 3: F = 27 + 32

  Step 4: F = 59°

Example 4: Change 23 degrees Celsius to degrees Fahrenheit.

  Step 1: F = (9/5 x C) + 32

  Step 2: F = (9/5 x 23/1) + 32

  Step 3: F = 207/5 + 32 = 41.4 + 32

  Step 4: F = 73.4°

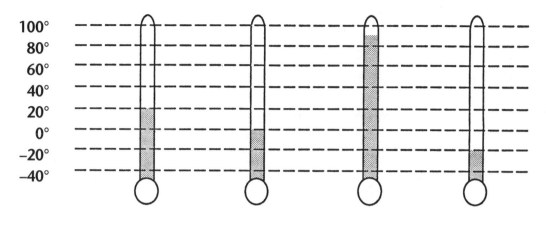

A Use the diagram below to read the correct temperatures. All are shown in degrees Celsius.

100°
80°
60°
40°
20°
0°
−20°
−40°

_____   _____   _____   _____

B Change the following Fahrenheit temperatures to degrees Celsius. Round your answer to the nearest tenth.

1. 38° F = _____

2. 49° F = _____

3. 82° F = _____

4. 95° F = _____

5. 212° F = _____

C Change the following Celsius temperatures to degrees Fahrenheit. Round your answers to the nearest tenth.

1. 0° C = _____

2. 10° C = _____

3. 20° C = _____

4. 59° C = _____

5. 100° C = _____

D Underline the warmer temperature in each pair.

1. 60° Fahrenheit or 15° Celsius   3. 27° Fahrenheit or 0° Celsius

2. 83° Fahrenheit or 23° Celsius   4. 109° Fahrenheit or 35° Celsius

Guide Question: What do scientists do with data from an experiment?

Vocabulary: average   grid line   line graph   vertical axis
bar graph   horizontal axis   pie graph

When scientists need to present the results of an experiment to others, they organize their data in special ways so that others can understand their results. By organizing the data, they can summarize it for others.

One method of summarizing data is to calculate an **average.** An average is one number that can describe an entire set of numbers. The average is calculated by adding the list of numbers together and then dividing that total by how many numbers were added. For example, you can find the test average in a class by adding all test scores together and then dividing the total by the number of tests.

Suppose you received the following test scores in a class.

Test Number	Score
1	87
2	92
3	74
4	78
5	65

To find the average, first add the scores:
87 + 92 + 74 + 78 + 65 = 396

Now divide the total by the number of tests, *five:*
396 ÷ 5 = 79.2

The average test score is 79.2.

Graphs are used to show data in relation to other data. They make data visible so that comparisons are easier to make. The test scores could be shown on a **bar graph.** A bar graph uses large bars to show quantities. Look at the bar graph below of a student's test scores.

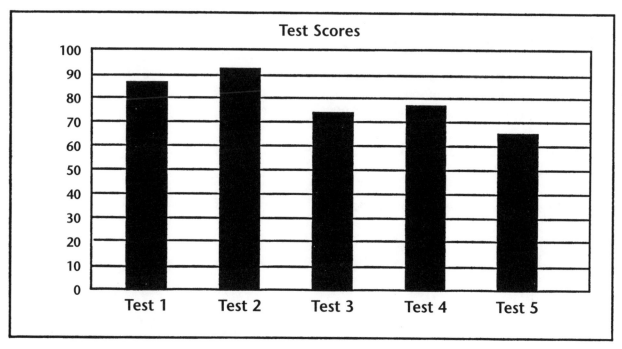

There are two important lines on a graph. These are called the axes of the graph. The first vertical line on the left of the graph is the **vertical axis.** The graph above shows the test score. The bottom horizontal line is the **horizontal axis,** and it shows the test number. All of the other lines are called **grid lines.** To read the graph, choose a test, find the top of the bar, and follow the grid line across to its score.

Some data is better shown on a **line graph.** For example, a record of the change in temperature could be shown on a line graph.

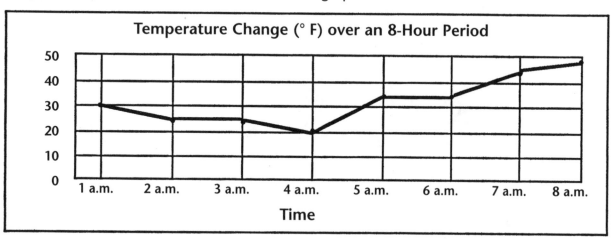

The graph at the bottom of page 23 provides a better picture of what actually happened to the temperature that morning because the line indicates the direction of the changing temperature. For example, the temperature at 5 a.m. was 35 degrees Fahrenheit and rising.

A third type of graph is a **pie graph.** This type is most often used to show the distribution of the individual items in a set of data. A distribution shows how many of each type of data there are. Pie graphs always show numbers as a percent of the total number of something. For example, a teacher might use a pie graph to show what percent of students scored in each grade category. The total pie graph represents the whole class, or 100%.

Imagine that there are 20 students in the class. Their grades on a test are as follows:

Grade	Number of Students	Percent of Total
A	4	20%
B	6	30%
C	6	30%
D	3	15%
F	1	5%
Total	20	100%

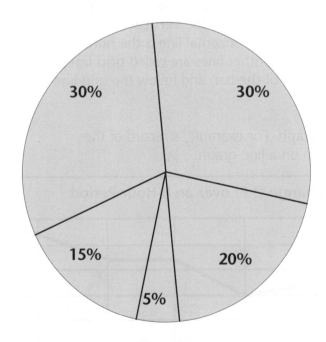

Suppose you started an exercise program. You walked on each of five days and recorded the following distances:

Day:	Monday	Tuesday	Wednesday	Thursday	Friday
Distance in miles:	3	5	2	6	1

A Make a bar graph to show the above data. Label the vertical and horizontal axes.

Exercise Chart

10					
9					
8					
7					
6					
5					
4					
3					
2					
1					
	Monday	Tuesday	Wednesday	Thursday	Friday

B Use your graph to answer the following questions.

1. On which day did you walk the greatest distance? _____

2. On which day did you walk the least distance? _____

3. What was the total number of miles walked for five days? _____

4. Which three days provided the most exercise? _____

   _____

5. Which two days provided the least exercise? _____

6. What is the difference between the greatest and the least days? _____

7. What is the average distance walked per day? _____

Review Unit 1

A Change each of the following measurements.

1. 5 meters = _____ centimeters

2. 650 millimeters = _____ meters

3. 2 grams = _____ milligrams

4. 30 kilograms = _____ grams

5. 6 liters = _____ centiliters

B Solve each problem that follows.

1. What is the density of an object with a weight of 32 grams if it has a volume of 4 cubic centimeters? _____

2. What is the temperature in Celsius if the temperature is 68 degrees Fahrenheit?
   _____

3. What is the temperature in Fahrenheit if the temperature is 165 degrees Celsius?
   _____

4. What is the average number of children in the first five grades of Crawford School if the first grade has 67 children, the second grade 72 children, the third grade 78 children, the fourth grade 69 children, and the fifth grade 64 children? _____

5. What is the volume of a cube that is 8 decimeters long, 4 decimeters wide, and 2 decimeters high? _____ cubic decimeters or_____ liters

C Make a pie chart to show the results of a survey about equipment most often used in a laboratory. Write the name of the piece of equipment and the percentage in each space you create on the pie chart.

The results were as follows:

graduated cylinder 50%
meter stick 15%
thermometer 25%
scale 10%

Use the clues to complete the crossword puzzle.

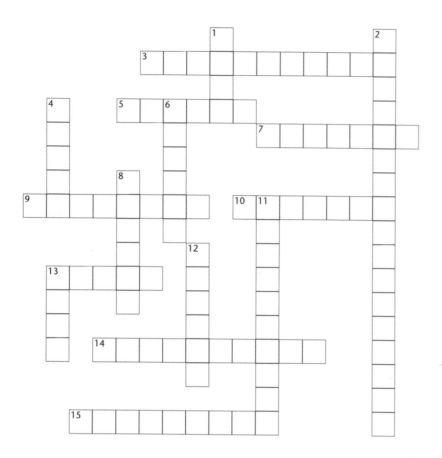

Across

3. records temperature
5. length times width times height
7. metric temperature scale
9. individual detail
10. type of scale for measuring mass
13. metric unit of length
14. scale on which water freezes at 32°
15. instrument that measures air pressure

Down

1. metric unit of mass
2. instrument that measures liquid volume
4. metric unit of liquid volume
6. how long something is
8. what we use to gather information
11. instrument for measuring wind speeds
12. unit of temperature
13. the amount of matter

**U
N
I
T

2**

Guide Question: What are atoms?

Vocabulary: atom   electron   neutron
         atomic mass   element   nucleus
         atomic number   mass number   proton

An **atom** is a basic unit of matter. All matter is made of atoms. Atoms are so small that they cannot be seen even with a microscope. Everything on earth is made of atoms: your hair, the paper you are reading, and the air between you and this page.

Since atoms cannot be seen, scientists use a model to describe their structure. An atom, according to the model, has a central part called the **nucleus.** The nucleus contains two types of particles, **protons** and **neutrons.**

Electrons surround the nucleus in layers like the layers of an onion. Each layer can hold a certain number of electrons. Electrons are very small particles, much smaller, in fact, than protons.

Most of an atom is empty space. The electrons are held in place by an electric charge. The protons in the nucleus are positively charged, and the electrons are negatively charged. Neutrons have no charge—they are neutral. The number of protons in an atom is equal to the number of electrons.

If everything is made of atoms, how can matter take so many different forms? The answer is that there are different kinds of atoms; they have different numbers of protons, neutrons, and electrons.

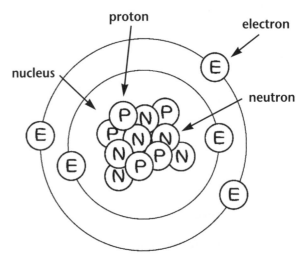

The Atom

The **elements** are the building blocks of matter. They form the four states or phases of matter: solid, liquid, gas, and plasma. There are 112 elements. Each one of these elements is different from the others because of its number of protons and electrons.

Each element is identified by an atomic number, an atomic mass, and a mass number. The **atomic number** tells how many protons are in the nucleus of the element. Hydrogen, a gas, is the simplest element. An atom of hydrogen contains one proton and one electron. Helium, another gas, contains two protons and two electrons. What is the atomic number of hydrogen? Since hydrogen has one proton, its atomic number is one. Helium, with two protons, has an atomic number of two.

The **atomic mass** of an element is a number based on the average weight of an atom of the element. The **mass number** is equal to the number of protons plus the number of neutrons.

A Write the correct word for each phrase.

1. The center of an atom _____

2. Equal to the number of electrons _____

3. Layered around the nucleus _____

4. The simplest element _____

5. The building blocks of matter _____

B Write the word that will make each sentence correct.

1. The _____ is equal to the number of _____ in the nucleus.

2. An atom of _____ contains two protons and two electrons.

3. The four states or phases of _____ are solid, liquid, gas, and plasma.

4. There are 112 _____.

5. The average weight of an atom is the _____.

C Fill in the missing parts of this table of the elements.

Element	Protons	Electrons	Atomic Number
Aluminum	13	13	
Lead		82	82
Carbon			6

Guide Question: What are chemical symbols?

Vocabulary: abbreviation   symbol

In chemistry, each element has an **abbreviation** called a **symbol**. A symbol is made up of one, two, or three letters that stand for the element's name. By using symbols, scientists can save time and space when writing about the elements.

Here are some rules that will help you learn the symbols for elements:

Rule 1   Most symbols have either one or two letters. A few symbols have three letters.

Rule 2   The first letter of a symbol is always capitalized.

Rule 3   If the symbol has two or three letters, the second and third letters are not capitalized.

Rule 4   No period is used after the symbol.

Here are some examples of symbols properly written.

Element Name	Element Symbol
hydrogen	H
helium	He
calcium	Ca
oxygen	O

There are 112 elements. Each of the elements (except for Elements 111 and 112) has its own symbol. For most elements, the symbol is either the first letter or the first two letters of the name (see above). Other elements have symbols that use the first letter and one or more letters found in the name, like these below.

Element Name	Element Symbol
chlorine	Cl
magnesium	Mg
arsenic	As
zinc	Zn

Finally, there are some elements whose symbols do not contain any letters found in their English names. These symbols usually come from the Latin names for the elements.

Element Name	Element Symbol
tin	Sn
lead	Pb
silver	Ag
gold	Au

A Refer to the charts on pages 30 and 31 to write the correct element name used in each sentence.

1. The baby was as good as (Au) _____ while her mother shopped.

2. Weedkillers may contain _____ (As), a deadly poison.

3. Milk is high in (Ca) _____.

4. Too much (Cl) _____ in a pool will burn your eyes.

5. The (He) _____ -filled balloon floated to the ceiling.

6. Homes should not be painted with paints that contain (Pb) _____.

7. In 1859, (Ag) _____ was discovered in Virginia City, Nevada.

8. We tied (Sn) _____ cans to the back of the car after the wedding.

B Refer to the charts on pages 30 and 31 to record the symbols for each of these elements.

1. silver _____

2. lead _____

3. gold _____

4. magnesium _____

5. calcium _____

6. helium _____

7. arsenic _____

8. zinc _____

C Refer to the charts on pages 30 and 31 to record the name of each element that is represented by the following symbols.

1. Sn _____

2. H _____

3. Cl _____

4. O _____

U
N
I
T

2

Guide Question: How are elements arranged in the Periodic Table?

Vocabulary: alkali metal   inert   noble gas
              halogen   metal   nonmetal

Many elements have similar properties. Chlorine and fluorine, for instance, are both poisonous gases. Copper, silver, and gold are all metals that conduct electricity. Because of these similar properties, the elements can be grouped into families and organized in a table that shows these common properties.

Noble gases

Alkali metals   **Nonmetals**   **Halogen**

1																		2
H																		He
1.0079																		4.0026

3	4											5	6	7	8	9	10
Li	Be											B	C	N	O	F	Ne
6.941	9.0122											10.81	12.011	14.0067	15.9994	18.9984	20.179

11	12											13	14	15	16	17	18
Na	Mg											Al	Si	P	S	Cl	Ar
22.9898	24.305											26.9815	28.086	30.9738	32.06	35.453	39.948

19	20	21	22	23	24	25	26	27	28	29	30	31	32	33	34	35	36
K	Ca	Sc	Ti	V	Cr	Mn	Fe	Co	Ni	Cu	Zn	Ga	Ge	As	Se	Br	Kr
39.098	40.08	44.9559	47.88	50.9415	51.996	54.938	55.847	58.9332	58.69	63.546	65.39	69.72	72.59	74.9216	78.96	79.904	83.80

37	38	39	40	41	42	43	44	45	46	47	48	49	50	51	52	53	54
Rb	Sr	Y	Zr	Nb	Mo	Tc	Ru	Rh	Pd	Ag	Cd	In	Sn	Sb	Te	I	Xe
85.4678	87.62	88.906	91.224	92.9064	95.94	(98)	101.07	102.906	106.42	107.868	112.41	114.82	118.71	121.75	127.60	126.905	131.29

55	56		72	73	74	75	76	77	78	79	80	81	82	83	84	85	86
Cs	Ba		Hf	Ta	W	Re	Os	Ir	Pt	Au	Hg	Tl	Pb	Bi	Po	At	Rn
132.905	137.33		178.49	180.948	183.85	186.207	190.2	192.22	195.08	196.967	200.59	204.383	207.2	208.980	(209)	(210)	(222)

87	88		104	105	106	107	108	109	110	111	112
Fr	Ra		Unq	Unp	Unh	Uns	Uno	Une	Uun		
(223)	226.025		(261)	(262)	(263)	(262)	(267)	(268)	(269)		

57	58	59	60	61	62	63	64	65	66	67	68	69	70	71
La	Ce	Pr	Nd	Pm	Sm	Eu	Gd	Tb	Dy	Ho	Er	Tm	Yb	Lu
138.91	140.12	140.908	144.24	(145)	150.36	151.96	157.25	158.925	162.50	164.93	167.26	168.934	173.04	174.967

89	90	91	92	93	94	95	96	97	98	99	100	101	102	103
Ac	Th	Pa	U	Np	Pu	Am	Cm	Bk	Cf	Es	Fm	Md	No	Lr
227.028	232.038	231.036	238.03	237.048	(244)	(243)	(247)	(247)	(251)	(252)	(257)	(258)	(259)	(260)

This table is called the *Periodic Table of the Elements,* or just the *Periodic Table.* The elements are arranged in order of increasing atomic number. The table shows elements with important common properties grouped in columns. It also divides the elements into two major groups, metals and nonmetals.

Metals are elements that are able to give up electrons in order to combine with other elements. Iron, for example, can combine with oxygen to form iron oxide (rust). **Nonmetals** are elements that gain electrons as they combine with other elements. Chlorine, for example, combines with sodium to form sodium chloride (table salt).

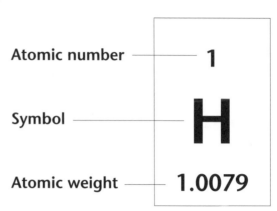

Atomic number — 1

Symbol — H

Atomic weight — 1.0079

The box shows specific information for hydrogen. All tables will show at least this much data about each element. Some provide more detailed information. These tables will usually have a sample like this one that shows what each number in the box means. Each column of the Periodic Table is called a family. Let's look at three families to see how they are related.

The members of the **alkali metal** family are lithium, sodium, potassium, rubidium, cesium, and francium. These elements are very active and will combine with many others. Each of them has one electron in its outer shell.

The chart below lists each of the elements by name and symbol.

Actinium	Ac	Copper	Cu	Lanthanum	La	Plutonium	Pu	Tellurium	Te
Aluminum	Al	Curium	Cm	Lawrencium	Lr	Polonium	Po	Terbium	Tb
Americium	Am	Dysprosium	Dy	Lead	Pb	Potassium	K	Thallium	Tl
Antimony	Sb	Einsteinium	Es	Lithium	Li	Praseodymium	Pr	Thorium	Th
Argon	Ar	Erbium	Er	Lutetium	Lu	Promethium	Pm	Thulium	Tm
Arsenic	As	Europium	Eu	Magnesium	Mg	Protactinium	Pa	Tin	Sn
Astatine	At	Fermium	Fm	Manganese	Mn	Radium	Ra	Titanium	Ti
Barium	Ba	Fluorine	F	Mendelevium	Md	Radon	Rn	Tungsten	W
Berkelium	Bk	Francium	Fr	Mercury	Hg	Rhenium	Re	Unnilennium	Une
Beryllium	Be	Gadolinium	Gd	Molybdenum	Mo	Rhodium	Rh	Unnilhexium	Unh
Bismuth	Bi	Gallium	Ga	Neodymium	Nd	Rubidium	Rb	Unniloctium	Uno
Boron	B	Germanium	Ge	Neon	Ne	Ruthenium	Ru	Unnilpentium	Unp
Bromine	Br	Gold	Au	Neptunium	Np	Samarium	Sm	Unnilquadium	Unq
Cadmium	Cd	Hafnium	Hf	Nickel	Ni	Scandium	Sc	Unnilseptium	Uns
Calcium	Ca	Helium	He	Niobium	Nb	Selenium	Se	Unununium	Uun
Californium	Cf	Holmium	Ho	Nitrogen	N	Silicon	Si	Uranium	U
Carbon	C	Hydrogen	H	Nobelium	No	Silver	Ag	Vanadium	V
Cerium	Ce	Indium	In	Osmium	Os	Sodium	Na	Xenon	Xe
Cesium	Cs	Iodine	I	Oxygen	O	Strontium	Sr	Ytterbium	Yb
Chlorine	Cl	Iridium	Ir	Palladium	Pd	Sulfur	S	Yttrium	Y
Chromium	Cr	Iron	Fe	Phosphorus	P	Tantalum	Ta	Zinc	Zn
Cobalt	Co	Krypton	Kr	Platinum	Pt	Technetium	Tc	Zirconium	Zr

The members of the **halogen** family are fluorine, chlorine, bromine, iodine, and astatine. These elements are also active and combine readily. Each of them has seven electrons in its outer shell. The halogens often combine with the members of the alkali metal family.

The members of the **noble gas** family are helium, neon, argon, krypton, xenon, and radon. All of these elements are gases. They do not usually react with other elements. This means that they are **inert** gases.

A Refer to the tables on page 32 and 33 to answer the following questions.

1. What are two inert elements? _____

2. Which element has the smallest atomic mass? _____

3. What are the two big groups into which elements can be divided? _____

   _____

4. What element has an atomic number of 79? _____

5. What is the atomic mass of calcium? _____

6. What elements are in the same family as oxygen? _____

7. What is the symbol for sodium? _____

8. What element is represented by the symbol K? _____

9. How many protons are in an atom of fluorine? (Remember: the atomic number tells the

   number of protons.) _____

Because of their properties, certain elements are valuable for particular purposes. The reflective quality of gold, for example, combined with its softness, has made it the first choice for fine jewelry for thousands of years. After it was found to be an excellent conductor of electricity, it was also used to make very thin electrical wire. Silicon was once thought to be useless for anything but making glass.

B Find *silicon* in an encyclopedia or on the World Wide Web. Use the lines below to write a short report on its properties and current uses.

_____

_____

_____

_____

Properties of Elements

Guide Question: What are some properties of elements?

Vocabulary: boiling point   density   melting point

Based on its properties, or characteristics, matter can be divided into different groups. Scientists sometimes use the following three properties to group matter:

- density
- boiling point
- melting point

At times, scientists are often called in to identify an element. For example, an unknown substance might be causing pollution in a stream. To identify elements in the stream, a scientist would use the known properties of elements.

One helpful property is **density.** The density of an element is a measure of how heavy it is compared to the same volume of other elements. For example, a one-cubic centimeter container of water weighs one gram. A cubic centimeter of gold weighs 19.3 grams. The density of gold, then, is 19.3 grams per cubic centimeter. The formula for calculating density is density equals mass divided by volume:

density = mass ÷ volume

Example: What is the density of an element with a mass of 443.9 grams and a volume of 23 cubic centimeters?

density = mass ÷ volume
     = 443.9 g ÷ 23 cc
     = 19.3 g/cc

The densities of two different elements may be so close that this property is not enough to identify the element. The additional properties of boiling point and melting point could be used to further identify it.

A liquid's **boiling point** is the temperature at which it begins to bubble. At that point, the liquid is changing into a gas.

Melting point is the temperature at which a solid begins to change into a liquid. The melting point of ice, a solid, is 0° Celsius (32° Fahrenheit). The ice then turns into water, a liquid, at this temperature. If we heat the water to 100° Celsius (212° Fahrenheit), it will boil and change to a gas, steam.

Use this chart to answer the questions below. Temperatures are in °C.

Element	Boiling Point	Melting Point	Density
Aluminum	2467°	660°	2.7
Calcium	1484°	839°	1.6
Chlorine	–35°	–101°	.003
Copper	2567°	1083°	8.96
Gold	2807°	1064°	19.3
Iodine	185°	114°	4.9
Lead	1740°	328°	11.4
Mercury	357°	–39°	13.5
Oxygen	–183°	–218°	.001
Sulfur	445°	113°	2.1

1. Which element has the highest boiling point? _____

2. Which element has the lowest melting point? _____

3. Which elements boil at a temperature below freezing? _____

4. Which two elements have the lowest density? _____

5. Which two elements have the greatest density? _____

6. Which element has the greatest difference between its boiling and melting points?

   _____

7. Which element has the least difference between its boiling and melting points?

   _____

8. At what temperature does copper boil? _____

9. Which element has a boiling point of 185°C? _____

10. At what temperature does oxygen melt? _____

11. Which element has a density of 2.1? _____

12. At –35°C, would chlorine start to melt or boil? _____

Formation of Compounds

Guide Question: How do elements form compounds?

Vocabulary: compound   molecule   radical

Elements can combine in two different ways: mixtures and compounds. In mixtures, the elements are simply combined together. Mixtures can easily be separated compared to compounds. In a compound, the elements are held together by electric charges in much the same way that a magnet attracts other magnets. They can only be separated by creating new chemical reactions.

A **compound** is two or more elements combined chemically to form a new substance. The new substance may have completely different properties than any of the original elements.

Sugar, a white solid crystal, is a compound made from hydrogen, carbon, and oxygen. None of these elements is sweet. Carbon is black. Hydrogen and oxygen are gases. The sweetness and white color of sugar are its own properties.

Compounds are represented by formulas in the same way that symbols represent elements. The formula shows what elements are found in the compound and how many atoms of each element are combined in each molecule of the compound. Just as the atom is the smallest unit of an element, a **molecule** is the smallest unit of a compound.

A formula is like a recipe. The recipe lists the ingredients and how much of each is necessary. Here is the formula for table salt (sodium chloride): NaCl

A Answer these questions.

1. What elements make up the compound known as table salt?

_____

Since there are no numbers in the formula, we can assume that the compound contains one atom of Na and one atom of Cl. When no number is shown, the number of atoms in a molecule is one. Look at this formula: $MgSO_4$

2. What three elements make up this compound?

_____

How many atoms of each element are there? Notice the subscript 4 in O_4. That means that there are four atoms of O for each single atom of Mg and S. $MgSO_4$ is the formula for the compound known as Epsom salts.

B List the formula, or recipe, for each of these compounds. The first one has been done for you.

1. CO_2 _____carbon—1 atom_____

                  _____oxygen—2 atoms_____

2. HCl   _____

              _____

3. $ZnCl_2$ _____

              _____

4. H_2SO_4 _____

              _____

5. CH_4 _____

              _____

Compounds are given names that come from the names of their elements. There are simple rules that you can use to name most of the more common compounds. First, all compounds have two names. The first name of the compound comes from the first element in the formula. A subscript after the first element does not affect the name. The second name follows these rules:

Rule 1 If the compound has only two elements, the second name is the name of the second element with the ending changed to "ide."
Examples:

Cl	chlorine becomes chlor*ide*	F	fluorine becomes fluor*ide*
S	sulfur becomes sulf*ide*	I	iodine become iod*ide*
Br	bromine becomes brom*ide*	O	oxygen becomes ox*ide*

Rule 2 If the compound has more than two elements, the second name is one of the following.

NO_3	nitrate
OH	hydroxide
PO_4	phosphate
CO_3	carbonate
SO_4	sulfate

The names listed in rule 2 are called **radicals.** Radicals are groups of atoms that act as if they were one element. When naming compounds that contain radicals, you will sometimes see the radical in parentheses and a subscript written outside. To correctly name these compounds, the numbers inside parentheses must match the number shown in the list for rule 2. The numbers outside the parentheses do not affect the name. *Examples:*

HCl   First name is hydrogen.
          Second name is chloride.
          hydrogen chloride

$MgSO_4$ First name is magnesium.
          Second name is sulfate.
          magnesium sulfate

$Al(OH)_3$ First name is aluminum.
          Second name is hydroxide.
          aluminum hydroxide

C Name the following compounds.

1. KCl   First name is _____.

          Second name is _____.

          Compound: _____

2. $Ba(OH)_2$ First name is _____.

          Second name is _____.

          Compound: _____

3. $AlCl_3$ First name is _____.

          Second name is _____.

          Compound: _____

4. $MgBr_2$ First name is _____.

          Second name is _____.

          Compound: _____

5. $CaCO_3$ First name is _____.

          Second name is _____.

          Compound: _____

Acids

Guide Question: What are the properties of an acid?

Vocabulary: acid   indicator   pH
   hydrogen   litmus paper

Acids form a group of chemical compounds. They are used

- to make various types of batteries
- in making household cleaners
- in the manufacture of other useful chemicals
- in many over-the-counter and prescription drugs

All acids have two important properties. First, they all contain the element **hydrogen** (symbol is H). Second, they all have a sour taste. *Never attempt to taste any chemicals because they can be harmful.*

Here is a list of some common acids, their formulas, and how they are used or where they are found.

Acid name	Formula	Use/Where It Is Found
hydrochloric acid	HCl	found in the stomach
sulfuric acid	H_2SO_4	found in car batteries
carbonic acid	H_2CO_3	used in carbonated drinks
hydrofluoric acid	HF	used to etch glass
acetic acid	$HC_2H_3O_2$	found in vinegar
boric acid	H_3BO_4	used as an eye wash

Acids have the ability to cause chemical reactions. Acids are classified based on their strength. Their strength is indicated by a scale of numbers called **pH.** The pH scale of acids ranges from 0 (very strong) to 7 (neutral). The numbers can be decimals, also.

Scientists use a special type of paper called **litmus paper** to determine whether a substance is an acid. Blue litmus paper will turn red if placed in an acid. However, the litmus will not show the acid's strength.

Many common substances can be used to show that a substance is an acid. These substances are called **indicators,** and they show the presence of an acid by changing colors.

Laboratory Exercise—Making an Indicator for Acids

Materials

1 head of red cabbage	1 pan
1 liter of water	10 test tubes (or jars)
bowl	colander or cheesecloth
jar with cover	hot plate
sample acids (vinegar, boric acid,	oven gloves
lemon juice, orange juice)	

Caution: Use oven gloves when handling hot materials.
Never drink or eat materials used in an experiment.

Procedure

1. Chop the head of cabbage into small pieces.
2. Place the cabbage in the pan and cover with water.
3. Boil the water for about 15 minutes, or until the water turns red.
4. Strain the water through a colander or through a piece of cheese cloth.
5. Store extra liquid in a covered jar.
6. Place some drops (10–20) of the red indicator liquid into each of the test tubes.
7. Add the acids (a few drops at a time) until a color change is seen. The red cabbage liquid will turn yellowish in the presence of acids.
8. Record the results in the data table.
9. Try the test with other household substances. Tell whether they are acids.

Substance Tested	Results with Red Cabbage Indicator

Answer the following review questions.

1. What are two properties of acids? _____

2. What scale is used to measure acid strength? _____

3. What is an indicator? _____

Bases

U N I T 2

Guide Questions: What are bases? How do they react with acids?

Vocabulary: base   neutralize   OH radical

Bases are another group of chemical compounds. Like acids, they have many uses. Bases have several properties in common. They have a bitter taste, an oily texture, and they usually contain an **OH radical.** An OH radical is an atom of oxygen and an atom of hydrogen that stay together and act as a single unit.

Bases are used in ways similar to acids. Many bases are used in cleaning solutions and in drain cleaners. Here is a list of some common bases.

Base Name	Formula	Used for/Where It Is Found
sodium hydroxide	$NaOH$	drain cleaners
calcium hydroxide	$Ca(OH)_2$	building materials
magnesium hydroxide	$Mg(OH)_2$	antacids
potassium hydroxide	KOH	soap

Bases can be identified by using red litmus paper. This red litmus paper will turn blue when a base is present. Bases also have a pH, the value of which will vary between 7 to 14. A value of 7 indicates a neutral substance such as water; a value of 14 indicates a strong base.

A Bases will be indicated when combined with the red cabbage solution that you made in the previous lesson. Combine some of the juice with each of the following liquids. Describe any changes that take place in color or appearance.

1. ammonia _____

_____

2. glass cleaner _____

_____

3. hand soap _____

_____

4. an antacid tablet _____

_____

Acids and bases **neutralize** each other when mixed. When an acid mixes with a base, water is formed and a new chemical appears that is neither an acid nor a base. In the lab activity below, you will neutralize an acid and a base.

Laboratory Exercise—Neutralizing an Acid and a Base

Heartburn, or acid indigestion, is caused by too much acid in the stomach. An antacid is taken to neutralize some of the acid and to relieve the burning feeling. The antacid (a base) combines with acid to produce water and another chemical. In this exercise, try to neutralize two different acids using two different bases.

Materials

white or cider vinegar	antacid tablet
lemon juice	small test tube
bicarbonate of soda	blue litmus paper

Caution: Never taste any substance used in an experiment.

Procedure

1. Place about 5 ml of vinegar in a test tube.
2. Test the vinegar (an acid) with a piece of litmus paper.
3. Begin adding bicarbonate of soda (a base) a little at a time.
4. Observe any reaction and describe it.
5. Continue adding the bicarbonate of soda until there is no more reaction.
6. When the reaction stops, test the solution again with litmus paper.
7. Repeat the experiment using lemon juice as the acid and an antacid tablet as the base. Crush the antacid tablet before adding it to the lemon juice.

B Interpret your results.

1. Describe the properties of the bicarbonate of soda. _____

    _____

2. Describe the properties of the vinegar. _____

    _____

3. Describe the reaction that occurs when the bicarbonate of soda is mixed with the vinegar.

    _____

    _____

4. What happens to the blue litmus paper when it is placed in the vinegar?_____

    _____

5. What happens to the blue litmus paper when the reaction no longer occurs? _____

    _____

Chemical Reactions

Guide Question: How do chemicals react?

Vocabulary: decomposition   single-replacement reaction

double-replacement reaction   synthesis

If you combine an inert gas, like neon, with a metal, like iron, nothing happens. No matter how long they are left together, nothing will happen. If iron is combined with water, it begins to rust. A chemical reaction takes place.

A chemical reaction takes place whenever one substance changes into a different substance. An element cannot be changed into another element, but compounds can be altered. There are four types of chemical reactions:

Synthesis Reactions

A **synthesis** reaction happens when two or more substances combine to form a third substance. For example, hydrogen gas will combine with oxygen gas to form water. This type of reaction can be shown as

$A + B \Rightarrow AB$

Example: hydrogen + oxygen $\Rightarrow$ Water

$H_2 + O \Rightarrow H_2O$

Decomposition Reactions

When a compound is broken down into two or more substances, a **decomposition** reaction has taken place. Decomposition can be thought of as separation. An example of a decomposition reaction is the breakdown of table salt, NaCl, to form solid sodium and chlorine gas. This type of reaction is shown as

$AB \Rightarrow A + B$

Example: table salt $\Rightarrow$ sodium + chlorine gas

$NaCl \Rightarrow Na + Cl$

Single-Replacement Reactions

A **single-replacement reaction** occurs when a single element replaces another element that is joined in a compound. The element that is replaced is set free. Suppose a scientist wants to have a quantity of hydrogen gas. Hydrogen is rarely found on Earth because it is lighter than air. It can be collected in a laboratory using a single-replacement reaction.

When the metal zinc is mixed with hydrochloric acid, the zinc joins with the chlorine to form zinc chloride. This releases the hydrogen as a gas. We can show this as

$A + BC \Rightarrow AC + B$

Example: zinc + hydrochloric acid $\Rightarrow$ zinc chloride + hydrogen

$Zn + HCl \Rightarrow ZnCl + H$

Double-Replacement Reactions

In a **double-replacement reaction**, two elements in different compounds switch places. When silver nitrate is mixed with sodium chloride, for example, a double replacement occurs. The sodium replaces the silver and becomes sodium nitrate, which is used as a food preservative. The silver replaces the sodium to form silver chloride. Silver chloride is used in making photographic film. The formula for a double replacement is

$AB + CD \Rightarrow AD + CB$

Example: silver nitrate + sodium chloride = sodium nitrate + silver chloride

$AgNO_3 + NaCl \Rightarrow NaNO_3 + AgCl$

A Use your understanding of reactions to match each phrase with its definition.

_____ 1. decomposition   a. two elements exchange

_____ 2. synthesis   b. separation of elements

_____ 3. double replacement   c. chemical change

_____ 4. single replacement   d. two elements join

_____ 5. reaction   e. one element released

B Label each type of reaction.

1. $AB \Rightarrow A + B$ _____

2. $A + B \Rightarrow AB$ _____

3. $AB + CD \Rightarrow AD + CB$ _____

4. $A + BC \Rightarrow AC + B$ _____

C Name the type of reaction.

1. $MgS \Rightarrow Mg + S$ _____

2. $NaCl + AgNO_3 \Rightarrow NaNO_3 + AgCl$ _____

3. $Fe + S \Rightarrow FeS$ _____

UNIT 2

Guide Question: How can you separate a mixture?

Vocabulary:

colloid	insoluble	solution
dissolve	mixture	solvent
heterogeneous	soluble	suspension
homogeneous		

A **mixture** is made of two or more elements or compounds. No chemical reaction takes place, so no new compounds are formed. The substances are simply mixed together. For example, air is a mixture of different gases. Concrete is a mixture of water, sand, gravel, crushed stone, and cement. Mixtures keep their separate identities and most of their own properties. They may change in physical appearance, but the substances do not change in chemical composition. Mixtures can be separated more easily than compounds.

There are different kinds of mixtures. A mixture that does not seem to be the same throughout is called a **heterogeneous** mixture. This kind of mixture is the "least mixed" of mixtures because its particles are large enough to be seen and large enough to be separated from the mixture. A pizza is an example. It is easy to see the parts of a pizza and to separate them.

A mixture that appears to be the same throughout is called a **homogeneous** mixture. The particles are "well mixed." They are very small and not easily recognizable. Homogeneous mixtures are also called **colloids.** Many things we eat and use every day are homogeneous mixtures. Milk and toothpaste are some examples.

A **solution** is one type of homogeneous mixture. A solution occurs when one substance **dissolves** in another. Water can be used as part of many mixtures that are solutions. Water and ammonia are mixed to form a cleaning solution for windows. Sea water is a mixture of salt and water. Lemonade and tea are also solutions. All solutions have several important properties. A solution has a substance that is dissolved and a substance that does the dissolving. Sugar, for instance, will dissolve when mixed with water. Baking soda also dissolves in water. Because so many substances dissolve in water, water is called the "universal **solvent.**" A substance that dissolves in liquid is said to be **soluble.** A substance that does not dissolve in liquid is said to be **insoluble.**

Some substances do not dissolve when mixed with a liquid. If you mix dirt and water, you can see the particles of dirt in the mixture. This kind of mixture is called a **suspension.**

Laboratory Exercise—Separating a Mixture of Salt and Sand

Materials
2 teaspoons of sand   2 teaspoons of salt
2 beakers or jars   1 piece of filter paper
glass of water   1 stirrer

Procedure
1. On a sheet of paper, thoroughly mix the salt with the sand.
2. Describe the resulting mixture.
3. Place the mixture in a beaker and cover it with water.
4. Stir the mixture to help the salt dissolve.
5. Place the filter paper across the top of the other beaker.
6. Slowly pour the mixture into the second beaker through the filter paper.
7. Allow the contents of the second beaker to sit for a few days or until the water evaporates.

A Interpret the results.

1. What happens to the salt when the water is added to the mixture?_____

   _____

2. What kind of mixture is this called? _____

   _____

3. What happens to the sand when the water is added to the mixture? _____

   _____

4. What is this mixture called?_____

   _____

5. Which material remains on the filter paper?_____

   _____

6. Which material is left in the second beaker after the water evaporates?

   _____

Laboratory Exercise—Separating a Mixture of Iron Filings and Sawdust

Materials
equal amounts of iron filings and sawdust
magnet
beaker of water
2 sheets of paper

Procedure

Experiment 1
1. On a sheet of paper, thoroughly mix the iron filings with the sawdust.
2. Place a magnet beneath the paper and gently move it back and forth.
3. Turn the paper sideways (keep the magnet in place) and shake the paper gently over another sheet of paper.
4. Repeat until the mixture is completely separated.

Experiment 2
1. Thoroughly mix the sawdust with the iron filings.
2. Slowly pour the mixture into the beaker of water.
3. Allow the contents of the beaker to sit for a few minutes.

B Interpret the results.

1. What happens to the sawdust when the magnet is held under the paper?_____
_____

2. What happens to the filings when the magnet is held under the paper?_____
_____

3. What property allows you to separate this mixture in this way? _____
_____

4. Which material remains on the surface of the water in the beaker? _____
_____

5. What happens to the iron filings? Why? _____
_____

6. What property allows you to separate this mixture in this way? _____
_____

Review Unit 2

A Use the words in the box below to complete each sentence.

nucleus	atom	neutralize	symbol	element
compound	density	molecule	acid	base

1. _____ is the weight of a substance divided by its volume.

2. The smallest unit of matter, the_____, is so small it cannot be seen with a microscope.

3. The part of the atom that contains protons and neutrons is the

   _____.

4. In chemistry, each element has an abbreviation called its

   _____.

5. On the pH scale, a low number indicates the presence of a(n)

   _____.

6. A(n) _____ is the smallest unit of a compound.

7. The name of a(n) _____ comes from the elements that made it.

8. Often a(n) _____ is used in making soaps and cleaners.

9. The lightest _____ on the Periodic Table is hydrogen.

10. When an acid and a base are mixed, they will _____ each other.

B Unscramble each of the following groups of letters to complete each activity.

1. Identify the three states of matter.

   doisl _____

   uliidq _____

   ags _____

2. Name three major particles found in an atom.

   stcerlone _____

   snotrop _____

   nsortenu _____

C Write the atomic number of the element each symbol represents on the line. If all are correct, the sum of the numbers in each row, column, and diagonal will equal the atomic number of phosphorus. Refer to the Periodic Table on page 32.

___ O	___ H	___ C
___ Li	___ B	___ N
___ Be	___ F	___ He

D Use a term from the box to label each type of reaction.

double replacement	decomposition
single replacement	synthesis

1. AB + CD = AD + BC _____

2. AB = A + B _____

3. A + BC = AC + B _____

4. A + B = AB _____

5. $H_2O = H_2 + O$ _____

6. Na + Cl = NaCl _____

7. Zn + HCl = ZnCl + H _____

8. $AgNO_3 + NaCl = NaNO_3 + AgCl$ _____

Measuring Speed

Guide Question: How is speed measured?

Vocabulary: average speed   kilometers per hour   miles per hour
                  feet per second   meters per second

Suppose you travel in a car for two hours. In those two hours, you go a distance of 160 kilometers. Your average speed is equal to 80 kilometers per hour. **Average speed** is defined as the total distance traveled divided by the total time taken. The formula is:

$$s \text{ (average speed)} = d \text{ (distance)} \div t \text{ (time)}$$
$$s = d \div t$$
$$80 \text{ kph} = 160 \text{ kilometers} \div 2 \text{ hours}$$

Speed is measured in distance per time units such as:

Unit	Abbreviation
kilometers per hour	kph or k/h
meters per second	mps or m/s
miles per hour	mph or m/h
feet per second	fps or f/s

Speed may be measured in any other distance and time combination that you need. Those listed above are some of the most common.

The formula for average speed can also be used to find each of the other terms:

$d = s \times t$ $t = d \div s$

160 kilometers = 80 kph x 2 hours   2 hours = 160 kilometers ÷ 80 kph

Example: Suppose that you live 10 miles from school and are due there at 8:00 a.m. The speed limit is 30 miles per hour. How much time must you allow yourself to get to school on time?

$$t = d \div s = 10 \text{ miles} \div 30 \text{ mph} = 1/3 \text{ hour} = 20 \text{ minutes}$$

It is sometimes necessary to change speed units so that you can compare speeds measured in different units. For example, suppose you run the 100-meter dash in 10 seconds. How fast is that in kilometers per hour?

Step 1: Change 100 meters to kilometers.

100 meters = 100 ÷ 1,000 = .1 kilometers

(1 km = 1,000 meters)

Step 2: Change 10 seconds into hours.

10 seconds = 10 ÷ 3,600 = .003 hours

Step 3: Divide the number of kilometers by the number of hours.

.1 ÷ .003 hours = 33.3 kilometers per hour

If a car is traveling at 50 miles per hour, how many feet does it travel in 1 second?

Step 1: Change 50 miles into feet.

50 miles x 5,280 feet = 264,000 feet

Step 2: Change 1 hour into seconds.

1 hour x 3,600 seconds = 3,600 seconds

Step 3: Divide the number of feet by the number of seconds.

264,000 feet ÷ 3,600 seconds = 73.3 fps (feet per second)

A Use your understanding of the speed formula to complete the following chart.

Distance Traveled	Time	Average Speed
35 miles	5 hours	
50 yards	10 seconds	
40 kilometers	8 seconds	
5 miles		5 mph
1,000 feet		10 fps
	3 hours	10 mph

B Answer this question.

If sound waves travel at a speed of about 335 meters per second, how far

will a sound wave travel in 3 seconds? _____

Acceleration

Lesson 17

Guide Question: What is acceleration?

Vocabulary: acceleration deceleration

When you go on an automobile trip, you can calculate your average speed by dividing the total distance traveled by the time required for the trip. The average speed gives information about the whole trip.

Suppose you traveled a total of 200 kilometers in 4 hours. Your average speed is 50 kph. The average speed of 50 kph does not mean that you always traveled at 50 kph; your speed may have varied a great deal. In fact, you may have stopped to get gas or a drink of water. While stopped, your speed was 0 kph.

Most types of motion involve changing speeds. The increase in speed of an object is called acceleration. **Acceleration** means "increase in speed."

Here is the mathematical formula for calculating the rate of an object's acceleration:

acceleration = change in speed ÷ time required for the change
$a = \Delta s \div t$

Example: What is the acceleration of a car that goes from 25 kph to 30 kph in 5 seconds?

a = (30 kph – 25 kph) ÷ 5 s
a = 5 kph ÷ 5 s
a = 1 kph/s

The answer, 1 kph per second, means that the speed was increasing by one kilometer per hour each second.

Objects can also slow down. When this happens, the acceleration is said to be negative. Another word for slowing down is **deceleration.**

Example: What is the deceleration of an airplane that slows down from 600 mph to 180 mph in 100 seconds?

d = (600 mph – 180 mph) ÷ 100 s
d = 420 mph ÷ 100 s
d = 4.2 mph/s

The plane is slowing down, so the deceleration is 4.2 mph per second. This is the same as saying that the plane had a *negative* acceleration, a = – 4.2 mph/s.

A Fill in the missing information in this data table on acceleration.

Beginning Speed	Ending Speed	Time Taken	Acceleration
25 mph	45 mph	4 seconds	
30 mph	28 mph	2 seconds	
180 mph	120 mph	30 seconds	
50 kph	55 kph	5 seconds	
0 mph	10 mph	2 seconds	
0 kph	25 kph	10 seconds	
13 mph	19 mph	3 seconds	
5 mph	20 mph	2 seconds	

B Answer the following questions.

1. A car is traveling at 55 kph. The speed is increased to 75 kph. If the time needed to change speed is 4 seconds, what is the acceleration? _____

2. A car is traveling at 40 kph. The driver suddenly slams on the brakes and comes to a complete stop. (The speed is 0.) If it takes the car 4 seconds to stop, what is the deceleration? _____

3. A train is traveling at 60 mph. As it approaches a station, it slows to 10 mph, taking 50 seconds to slow to the lower speed. What is the deceleration? _____

4. A bicycle rider is traveling at 15 mph. A steep hill is ahead. It takes the rider 20 seconds to reach the top of the hill, at which time the rider's speed is 5 mph. What is the deceleration? _____

5. A truck is on an expressway ramp going 65 kph. The driver speeds up to 80 kph in 10 seconds in order to merge with traffic. What is the acceleration?

   _____

6. A plane is traveling 300 mph. If it accelerates at 10 mph per second (10 mph/s), how fast will it be going after 10 seconds? _____

Measuring Force

Guide Questions: What are forces? How are they measured?

Vocabulary: force   newton   pound

Whenever an object changes speed, a force must be present to cause the change. You probably have noticed a force like this many times. When your car is stopped at a traffic light and then begins to accelerate, you can feel this force push you back into the seat. The engine provides the force that moves the car.

If you watch people standing on a bus or subway as it comes to a stop, you can see them leaning forward. The brakes supply the force that stops the bus or train.

Force is often defined as a "push or pull." One force that operates everywhere on the earth is *gravity.* Every object on the earth is pulled toward the center of the planet by its gravitational force. The closer to the center of the earth an object is, the stronger the pull of gravity.

We measure the pull of the earth's gravity by weighing objects. Your weight is actually a measure of how strongly the earth is pulling you. In the English system, force is measured in **pounds.** In the metric system, force is measured in newtons. A **newton** is a force that will cause a mass of one kilogram to accelerate at one meter per second per second. The newton is the unit most often used by physical scientists.

Force and acceleration are closely related. If acceleration occurs, there is a force that causes it. This is shown mathematically in the following formula:

acceleration = force ÷ mass
a = f ÷ m

Example 1:   If an object has a mass of 5 kilograms and is pushed by a force of 10 newtons, what will the acceleration be?

a = f ÷ m = 10 newtons ÷ 5 kg = 2 meters/sec/sec

Example 2:   If the same object as in example 1 is pushed by a force of 20 newtons, what will the acceleration be?

a = f ÷ m = 20 newtons ÷ 5 kg = 4 meters/sec/sec

Example 3:   If an object has a mass of 10 kilograms and is pushed by a force of 10 newtons, what will the acceleration be?

a = f ÷ m = 10 newtons ÷ 10 kg = 1 meter/sec/sec

From the examples, can you see that the larger the mass, the greater the force needed to accelerate it? Also, a larger mass acted on by the same force will accelerate less than a smaller mass.

A Complete the following activities.

1. In what unit do we usually measure the force of the earth's gravity? _____

2. What is the preferred unit for measuring force in physical science? _____

3. Define the word *force.*_____

_____

4. Describe the difference in acceleration when the same force is applied to a mass of 5 kilograms and 50 kilograms. Why does this occur? _____

_____

_____

_____

5. Think of ways that things can be made to accelerate. List three forces that produce acceleration.

a. _____

b. _____

c. _____

B Solve the following problems that relate to acceleration.

1. A mass of 15 kilograms is pushed by a force of 30 newtons. How much does it accelerate?

_____

2. An object has a mass of 2 kilograms and is acted on by a force of 10 newtons. How much does the object accelerate? _____

3. A force of 30 newtons is applied to an object with a mass that is 5 kilograms. How much does the object accelerate? _____

4. Which accelerates more? A mass of 50 kilograms pushed by a force of 100 newtons or a mass of 20 kilograms pushed by a force of 30 newtons? _____

Guide Question: How do falling objects accelerate?

Vocabulary: g   gravitational acceleration

For thousands of years, people believed that larger, heavier objects would fall more quickly to the ground than lighter objects. Around the year 1600, a scientist named Galileo decided to test this theory. Galileo supposedly took different objects to the top of the Leaning Tower of Pisa and dropped them to the ground. He measured the time that they took to drop.

What he found was startling. All the objects took the same amount of time to fall, regardless of their size and weight! This same experiment has been repeated many times since, and the results have always been the same. Every object accelerates toward the earth at the same rate.

This acceleration is due to the pull of the earth's gravity and is known as **gravitational acceleration.** It is represented by the letter **g,** and on the earth's surface, it has a value of 32 feet per second per second in the English system or 9.8 meters per second per second in the metric system.

If no air resistance existed, all objects would continue to accelerate until they hit the ground. If dropped from the same height, objects would have the same speed at that moment.

The speed of a falling object can be found using the following formula:

speed = gravitational acceleration x time

$s = g \times t$

Example 1:   How fast will an object fall—in feet per second—after 5 seconds?

$s = g \times t$

s = 32 feet/sec/sec x 5 seconds

s = 160 feet per second

Example 2:   How fast will an object fall—in meters per second—after 8 seconds?

$s = g \times t$

s = 9.8 meters/sec/sec x 8 seconds

s = 78.4 meters per second

UNIT 3

Example 3: If an object is falling at a rate of 160 feet per second, how fast will it be traveling after 3 additional seconds?

s = g x t

s = 32 feet/sec/sec x 3 seconds

s = 96 feet per second

new speed = 160 feet/sec + 96 feet/sec = 256 feet/sec

Use your understanding of the speed formula to solve the following problems. You may use a calculator.

1. How fast will an object be falling after 15 seconds? Answer in feet per second.

   s = g x t

   s = _____ feet/sec/sec x _____ seconds

   s = _____ feet per second

2. How fast will an object be falling after 12 seconds? Answer in meters per second.

   s = g x t

   s = _____ meters/sec/sec x _____ seconds

   s = _____ meters per second

3. An object is falling at a rate of 160 feet/second. How fast will it go after 5 more seconds?

   s = g x t

   s = _____ feet/sec/sec x _____ seconds

   s = _____ feet per second

   new speed = _____ f/s + _____ f/s = _____ f/s

4. How fast will an object be falling after 23 seconds? Answer in meters per second.

   s = g x t

   s = _____ meters/sec/sec x _____ seconds

   s = _____ meters per second

5. How fast will an object be falling after 1 minute? Answer in feet per second. (Be sure to change 1 minute into seconds.)

   s = g x t

   s = _____ feet/sec/sec x _____ seconds

   s = _____ feet per second

Guide Question: What are Newton's Three Laws of Motion?

Vocabulary: action   reaction   resistance
                 friction   recoil

Sir Isaac Newton, a scientist who lived in the 1600s, did important work in physical science. He is well-known for his study of forces and how they affect matter. He developed three principles that are now known as Newton's Laws of Motion.

> **Law Number One:** All objects remain at rest or move at constant speed in a straight line unless acted upon by an outside force.

Any object that is sitting still will stay that way until a force acts on it. A rock lying on the ground does not begin moving all by itself. A force is required to accelerate the rock. When a pitcher throws a baseball, it moves in a straight line toward the catcher. The ball will continue in this direction until the batter hits it or the catcher stops it with his glove.

According to the first law, it might seem that the ball should never hit the ground. Of course, we know that the ball eventually slows down and stops. What stops it?

First, there is the force of gravity that pulls the ball down. Second, the force of **friction**, caused by air **resistance**, also slows down the ball. If the ball were thrown in outer space, away from the pull of gravity and air friction, it would continue to move forever.

> **Law Number Two:** The acceleration of an object depends on the force acting on it and the mass of the object.

This law is the source of the formula we used in the previous lesson to measure acceleration.

> **Law Number Three:** For every force there is an equal and opposite force. Every **action** has a **reaction.**

Law Number Three can be illustrated by what happens when a cannon is fired. The cannonball is accelerated from the barrel by the force of the explosion. The barrel is pushed backward with an equal force. This is called the **recoil.** Because the body of the cannon is so much larger than the ball, the ball is accelerated much more than the cannon.

Measuring Work

UNIT 3

Guide Questions: What is work? How is it measured?

Vocabulary: foot-pound   kinetic   work

joule   potential

Suppose you awake feeling great one morning. You are full of energy and want to be active. You might rearrange your room, build something, or wash the car. This energy is stored in your body, waiting to be used. Scientists would call it potential energy.

Potential energy is stored energy. A battery is an example of stored energy because it can provide power. A spring is another example of potential energy, because when it is pulled and let go, the energy stored in it is released. Can you think of other examples?

Kinetic energy is the energy of motion. When potential energy is released, it becomes kinetic energy. For example, the energy stored in your muscles becomes kinetic energy when used to pedal a bike.

Once you decide what you are going to do, you start to work. Your energy is not just potential; it is now kinetic energy. Kinetic energy is energy in action.

We use six forms of energy to do work.

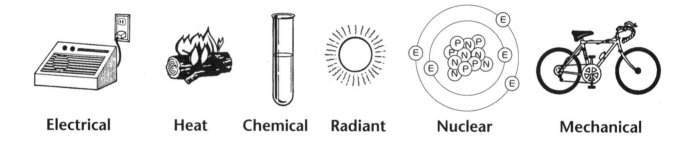

| Electrical | Heat | Chemical | Radiant | Nuclear | Mechanical |

Energy is used to do work. **Work** is defined in physics as a force moving an object. For work to be done, an object must move as a result of a force. If 500 pounds of force is applied to a rock and it does not move, no work has been done. The formula for calculating work done is

work = force applied x distance moved
w = f x d

In the English system, force is measured in pounds. The distance is usually measured in feet. The unit of work, pounds times feet, is the **foot-pound.** The metric unit of work is the **joule.**

Example 1: How much work is done when a concrete block weighing 50 pounds is lifted 2 feet?

W = f x d

W = 50 pounds x 2 feet

W = 100 foot-pounds

Example 2: How much work is done when you push a car 20 meters with 100 newtons of force?

W = f x d

W = 100 newtons x 20 meters

W = 2,000 joules

A Solve these problems. You may use a calculator.

1. How much work is done when pushing a rock a distance of 12 meters with 200 newtons of force? _____

2. How much work is done picking up a box of records weighing 43 pounds if you place it on a shelf 4 feet high? _____

3. A girl did 1,000 foot-pounds of work with a force of 10 pounds. How far did she move the object? _____

B Review your understanding of the concept of work. Complete the activities that follow.

1. Explain the difference between potential and kinetic energy.

_____

_____

2. Name the six forms of energy.

_____

3. Before reading this lesson, how would you have defined *work?* How is the physical science definition of work different from your own definition?

_____

_____

U N I T 3

Guide Question: What are simple machines?

Vocabulary: fulcrum   mechanical advantage   simple machine

inclined plane   pulley   wedge

lever   screw   wheel and axle

Simple machines are devices that can improve our ability to do work. They work in three different ways:

- They can increase the force applied.
- They can increase the speed of an object.
- They can change the direction of an applied force.

An example of a simple machine that increases force is an automobile jack. By pressing down on the jack with a small force, the machine raises the car by multiplying the force applied. A baseball bat is a machine used to increase the speed of an object (the baseball). A pulley can be used to pick up an object by pulling down on a rope. The pulley has changed the direction of the force.

There are six different types of simple machines. Each of the six can be combined together in different ways to form compound machines. The six types are levers, pulleys, inclined planes, wedges, screws, and wheels and axles.

Lever

A **lever** is a bar that is free to rotate around a point called a **fulcrum**. Levers can be used for all three of the purposes listed above. Levers are classified into three groups depending on the location of the fulcrum, the object, and the force.

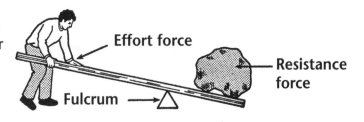

Pulley

A **pulley** is a wheel with a rope or string around it. It can be either fixed or movable. Fixed and movable pulleys can be combined to increase the force applied.

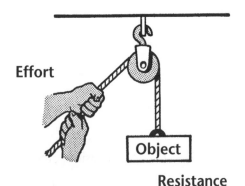

Inclined Plane

An **inclined plane** has no moving parts (see the illustration). It is easier to push something up an inclined plane (such as a ramp) than to lift it straight up. An inclined plane is also seen in two other machines, the screw and the wedge.

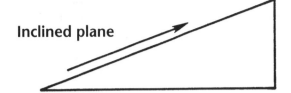

Inclined plane

Wedge

A **wedge** is two inclined planes joined together (see illustration). A wedge is useful in splitting logs for firewood. An ax is a metal wedge on the end of a wooden handle.

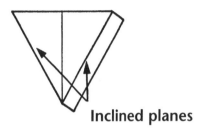

Inclined planes

Screw

A **screw** is an inclined plane wrapped around a pointed rod. Screws make it much easier to attach two objects together.

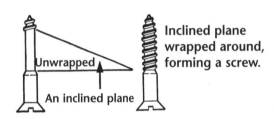

Unwrapped

An inclined plane

Inclined plane wrapped around, forming a screw.

Wheel and axle

An example of a **wheel and axle** is the steering wheel of a car. It can also be seen in the old-fashioned well. As the crank is turned the rope wraps around the axle, raising the bucket of water.

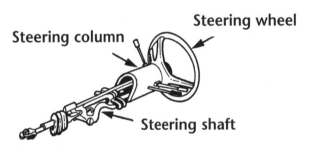

Steering column

Steering wheel

Steering shaft

All simple machines can be used to multiply force. The number of times a machine multiplies a force is called the **mechanical advantage**. To calculate the mechanical advantage of a simple machine, divide the resistance force moved by the effort force applied.

Example: What is the mechanical advantage of a lever that is used to raise a resistance force of 125 kilograms with an effort force of 25 kilograms?

mechanical advantage   =   resistance force ÷ effort force

                                      =   125 kg ÷ 25 kg

                                        =   5

UNIT 3

The mechanical advantage does not have any units. It is simply a number that tells how many times the force is multiplied.

Example: A machine has a mechanical advantage of 10. If you can apply 50 kilograms of force, what is the maximum resistance force you can move using this machine?

resistance force = mechanical advantage x effort force
= 10 x 50 kg
= 500 kg

A Unscramble each sentence. Write the sentence in its correct order on the line provided.

1. Mechanical is equal resistance to the force divided by the effort advantage force.

_____

2. work. improve Simple our machines ability to do

_____

B Complete the following activities.

1. Give an example of the use of each of the six simple machines.

Lever: _____

Pulley: _____

Inclined plane: _____

Screw: _____

Wedge: _____

Wheel and axle: _____

2. List the three advantages machines can provide.

a. _____

b. _____

c. _____

3. What is the mechanical advantage of a lever used to lift a resistance of 85 pounds with an effort of 5 pounds? _____

Using a Lever

Guide Question: How can you lift a heavier object with less force?

Laboratory Exercise—Changing the Mechanical Advantage of a Lever

Materials
piece of wood—1.5 meters x 1.5 centimeters (about 5 feet x .5 inches)
triangular fulcrum, or suitable block of wood between 7.5 and 12.5
    centimeters (3 and 5 inches) in height
2.3-kilogram (5-pound) sack of sand

Procedure
1. Place the fulcrum about 30 centimeters (12 inches) from one end of the board (the lever).
2. Place the sack of sand on the end of the lever closest to the fulcrum. (See **a.**)
3. Place your hand at the other end of the lever.
4. Push down on the lever to raise the sack of sand.
5. Move the fulcrum to the middle of the lever. (See **b.**)
6. Push down on the lever again to raise the sack of sand.
7. Move the fulcrum so that it is about 30 centimeters (12 inches) from your hand. (See **c.**)
8. Push down on the lever again to raise the sack of sand.

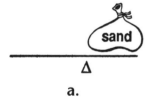

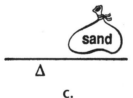

a.   b.   c.

 Interpret the results.

1. Look at the diagrams above. In which diagram is the least amount of force used?_____

2. In which diagram is the job most difficult?_____

3. How do you move the fulcrum of a lever to increase mechanical advantage?

_____

UNIT 3

Guide Question: What is the difference between heat and temperature?

Vocabulary: calorie   heat   temperature

Heat and temperature are not the same thing. You can show this by measuring the temperature of a wooden match and comparing it to the temperature of a bonfire made of wood. They both have the same temperature, but which one would you use to keep warm on a cold day? Which has more heat?

Temperature is actually a measure of the movement of molecules. The faster the molecules move, the higher the temperature. Heat depends on temperature and also on the amount of matter at a given temperature. Therefore, **heat** is equal to the change in temperature multiplied by the mass.

H = m x Δt

H is the heat measured in calories, *m* is the mass in grams, and Δ*t* is the change in temperature in degrees Celsius.

A *calorie* is a very small unit of heat energy. One **calorie** (1 c) is the amount of heat energy needed to raise the temperature of one gram of water by one degree Celsius. One *food calorie* (1 C) is equal to 1,000 calories (1,000 c) of heat energy.

Example 1:   How much heat is needed to raise the temperature of 50 grams of water from 19 to 23 degrees Celsius?

   H = m x Δt
   H = 50 grams x (23–19) degrees
   H = 50 grams x 4 degrees
   H = 200 calories

Heat can also be lost or given off by an object. When the temperature of water goes from 25 degrees to 2 degrees Celsius, heat is lost.

Example 2: How much heat is lost or given off when 50 grams of water is cooled from 25 to 20 degrees Celsius?

$$H = m \times \Delta t$$
$$H = 50 \text{ grams} \times (25{-}20) \text{ degrees}$$
$$H = 50 \text{ grams} \times -5 \text{ degrees}$$
$$H = -250 \text{ calories}$$

The minus sign means that heat is lost instead of gained.

A Use your knowledge of heat and temperature to fill in the blanks.

1. _____ is measured in calories.

2. A food calorie equals _____ heat calories.

3. _____ measures the movement of molecules.

4. The _____ molecules move, the higher the temperature.

5. The movement of molecules is measured in _____.

6. _____ measures temperature change times mass.

7. In the formula for calculating heat, mass is measured in _____.

B Use your knowledge of heat and temperature to solve the following problems.

1. How much heat is gained by 75 grams of water if the temperature goes from 10 to 35 degrees Celsius? _____

2. How much heat is lost when 500 grams of water is cooled from 28 to 0 degrees Celsius? _____

3. How much heat is lost by 50 grams of water if the temperature drops from 10 degrees Celsius to 0 degrees? _____

4. How much heat is needed to raise the temperature of 65 grams of water from 32 to 38 degrees Celsius? _____

5. How much heat is lost when 250 grams of water is cooled from 85 to 65 degrees Celsius? _____

Guide Question: How does heat travel?

Vocabulary: conduction   convection   radiation

Suppose you are camping in the fall. As evening comes, you build a fire; everyone gathers around it. If you were chilly, you would stand closer to the fire, but you would never touch it. How does the heat get from the fire to you?

The heat from the fire travels through the air. It radiates, or pushes out, in all directions. The closer you get to the fire, the warmer the air. This is one way heat travels. It is called **radiation.** The heat from the sun radiates through space all the way to the earth and beyond.

Radiation

If you put a hot dog on a stick, you can roast it in the fire. Your hand is safe because the wood does not conduct much heat. If you tried this with a metal rod, the heat would travel through the rod and burn your hand. A metal rod is a good heat conductor. The transfer of heat through material is called **conduction.**

Conduction

Why does the smoke from your campfire rise if there is no wind? It never lies on the ground around the fire. The smoke contains warm air. Warm air always rises, and cold air always falls. The transfer of heat through the movement of heated air or liquid is called **convection.**

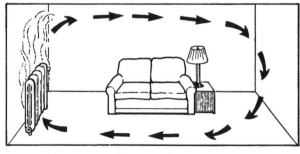

Convection

Laboratory Exercise—Determining How Heat Travels

Materials
4 olive jars (or suitable substitute)
food coloring (any color)
30.5 centimeters (1 foot) of copper tubing (or other metal tubing)
6 small birthday candles
1 Bunsen burner (or large candle)
1 ring stand with clamp
2 index cards
1 100-watt light bulb
1 shoe box
1 lab thermometer

Caution: Do not touch the lit bulb, heated tubing, or candlewicks.

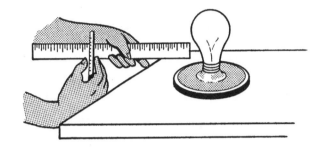

Procedure

Step 1: Observe radiation.

1. Connect the 100-watt bulb to a socket that can sit on a lab table.
2. Lay a ruler next to the bulb.
3. Hold the thermometer at the end of the ruler, away from the bulb.
4. Wait one minute and then record the temperature in the data table below.
5. Move the thermometer 5 centimeters (2 inches) closer to the bulb and record the temperature again.
6. Continue the procedure until you have completed the data table.

Radiant Heat Record	
Distance	**Temperature**
30.5 cm (12 in.)	
25.5 cm (10 in.)	
20.5 cm (8 in.)	
15 cm (6 in.)	
10 cm (4 in.)	
5 cm (2 in.)	

Step 2: Observe conduction.
1. Place the copper tube in the clamp on the ring stand.
2. Use the Bunsen burner to melt the bottom of each small candle slightly so that it will stick to the tube. Press each candle against the tube until it sticks.
3. Heat one end of the copper tube and observe the small candles.

Step 3: Observe convection.
1. Fill two of the jars with cold water.
2. Fill the other two jars with hot water.
3. Place three drops of food coloring in one jar of hot water and three drops in one jar of cold water.
4. Place an index card over the top of the clear jar of hot water.
5. Turn the jar over and place it on top of the colored cold water.
6. Remove the index card carefully and allow the jars to sit.
7. Repeat the process with the other two jars, keeping the colored jar on the bottom.

Interpret the results.

1. *Radiation.* Write a statement about how radiant heat is related to the distance from the source.

_____

_____

_____

2. *Conduction.* What happened to the candles? Were you able to follow the heat as it traveled through the tube?

_____

_____

_____

3. *Convection.* Explain the difference in the two results. Why do you think this difference occurred?

_____

_____

_____

Sound

Guide Question: What is sound?

Vocabulary:
acoustics	hertz	quality
decibel	intensity	sound wave
frequency	pitch	vibrate

Drop a pebble into a pond and watch the surface of the water. The pebble makes a force that causes ripples or waves. The waves travel out from the point where the pebble hit the water. Traveling in all directions, they become smaller and smaller until they disappear.

Like water, sound travels in waves.

Sound travels in **sound waves**. Sound is produced when an object vibrates, causing particles of air around the object to vibrate also. **Vibrate** means to move back and forth. As the vibration moves away from the source, it loses strength until it eventually cannot be heard.

How do you hear sounds? Inside your ear is a thin layer of cells stretched across the ear opening. This layer is like the head of a drum and is, in fact, called the eardrum. Vibrations in the air cause the eardrum to vibrate. Since the eardrum is extremely thin and sensitive, it can be easily punctured or scratched. This is why it is dangerous to place anything in your ear. If your eardrum is damaged, you may lose some of your hearing.

Sound waves travel through the air.

When sound travels from the drum to the eardrum, the vibration of air molecules carries the sound wave between the drum and the eardrum. The greater the number of molecules in the material a sound passes through, the faster the sound will travel. Underwater, sound travels faster than it does in air. Sound travels more quickly across water molecules because they are closer together and vibrate against one another more than air molecules do. If there are no molecules, sound cannot travel. In the vacuum of outer space, sound does not travel at all.

The science of sound is called **acoustics.** Scientists who study acoustics have determined that the speed of sound depends on the material that the sound travels through. The speed is also affected by the temperature. The following chart shows the speed of sound through some different materials.

Speed of Sound through Different Materials at 25° Celsius		
Material	**Speed (Meters/Sec)**	**Speed (Miles/Hr.)**
Steel	5,200	11,632
Wood	1,850	4,138
Water	1,497	3,349
Air	346	774

Another property of sound is **intensity.** The intensity is the force of the sound waves. The greater the vibration of the object producing the sound, the greater the intensity of the sound. Intensity is measured in **decibels.** *Loudness* depends upon the eardrum and hearing of the person listening. The following chart will give you an idea of different decibel levels.

Source	**Decibels (dB)**
rustling leaves	10
whisper	20
average home noise	35
normal conversation	65
vacuum cleaner	75
tractor	90
live rock music	115
thunder	130

In addition to loudness, sounds also have pitch. **Pitch** means the "highness" or "lowness" of a sound. For example, think of the sound made by a flute. We would describe that sound as having a high pitch. Now think of the sound from a bass guitar. That sound is described as having a low pitch.

Pitch always refers to how a person hears a sound. The property of sound that causes us to hear different pitches is **frequency.** The frequency of a sound is the number of waves that pass a given point in one second. For example, the lowest note that most people can hear has a frequency of 20 cycles (waves) per second.

A **hertz** is the unit used to measure sound frequency. A sound with a frequency of 20 hertz vibrates at 20 cycles per second. It has a low pitch, like the sound of a string bass in an orchestra.

A sound with a frequency of 20,000 hertz has a high pitch. The highest note that can be heard by most people has a frequency of 20,000 cycles per second, or 20,000 hertz.

Can you imagine the sound of a violin playing? Can you tell the difference between the sounds of a violin and a piano? Even when the violin and the piano play a note with the same frequency, you can tell them apart. They do not sound the same because each instrument produces its note in a different way or by using different materials. The violin makes a sound when a string vibrates and causes the wood in the body of the instrument to vibrate also. This makes a sound quite different from the sound of a piano note, which results from the striking of a string with a hammer. This difference is referred to as a difference in sound **quality.**

A Use your understanding of sound to complete the following exercises. Match each word with its correct definition.

_____ 1. hertz   **a.** unit of sound intensity

_____ 2. frequency   **b.** to move back and forth

_____ 3. vibrate   **c.** the science of sound

_____ 4. decibel   **d.** the number of sound waves that pass a given point each second

_____ 5. acoustics   **e.** unit of frequency

B Describe how *vibration* is created in each of the following instruments. Also, describe the quality of each. The first one has been done for you. Use complete sentences.

1. trombone _____ *Vibration is caused by air being forced through metal cylinders.*
   *The quality is a low, muffled sound.*

2. harp _____

3. saxophone _____

4. kettledrum _____

C Choose the correct word in the box to fill in the blanks. One word will be used twice.

vibrate	vibrations	vibrating
acoustics	acoustical	intense
intensity	frequency	frequently

1. _____ is the force of sound waves.

2. When a sound has a higher pitch, the waves arrive more _____.

3. _____ objects are the sources of sounds.

4. When sound waves travel, molecules in the air _____.

5. Scientists who study _____ examine the properties of sound.

6. Sound _____ travel faster through steel than through air.

7. A piano's sound is produced when its strings are hit by small hammers, which cause the strings to _____.

8. _____ tile is used in ceilings to absorb sound waves.

9. The more _____ a sound is, the louder it seems.

10. The highest _____ that most people can hear is 20,000 hertz.

D Sonar is used by ships at sea to tell how deep the water is and how far away objects are. A sound wave is transmitted (sent out); it reflects off an object back to the ship. The time the echo takes to return to the ship is used to calculate the distance of the object. The number of seconds the echo takes to return is divided by two and then multiplied by the speed of sound in water. Check the chart on page 72 to determine the speed of sound in water. Then solve the sonar problems. Use the formula: distance = [time in seconds ÷ 2] x speed of sound in water.

1. How deep is the water if the sound wave sent to the bottom takes two seconds to return?

_____ meters

2. How far away is a submarine if the echo returns in ten seconds? _____ meters

Laboratory Exercise—Make a String Telephone

String telephone

Materials
2 tin cans
2 Styrofoam cups
2 buttons
15 meters (about 50 feet) of string
a block of paraffin wax

Procedure
1. Punch a hole in the bottom of each can.
2. Push the end of the string through the hole and tie it to a button on the inside of the can, as shown in the picture. Repeat with the other end of the string and the second can.
3. With a partner, stretch the string to its full length and then talk into and listen through the cans.
4. Wax the string with the paraffin block. Does the sound quality improve?
5. Touch the string with your finger as you talk. What effect does this have on the sound quality?
6. Try making another phone with Styrofoam cups, but do not use buttons. Simply tie large knots in the ends of the string. Compare the sound quality of the two types. Is there any difference in the quality between a phone made from tin cans and one made from the Styrofoam cups?

Laboratory Exercise—Experiment with Tuning Forks

Materials
set of tuning forks
a pan of water

Tuning fork

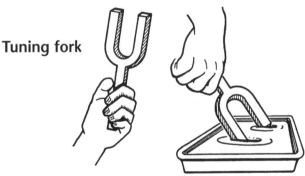

Procedure
1. Holding a tuning fork at its end, strike it against a hard surface like a countertop.
2. Listen to the sound (you may have to hold the fork close to your ear).
3. Take a tuning fork in each hand and strike both against a hard surface at the same time. What kind of sound is produced?
4. Hold one tuning fork in your hand. Place the bottom of the other tuning fork against a countertop. Which one produces a louder sound when struck? Why?
5. After striking one of the tuning forks, place its tip in a pan of water. Describe what happens to the water. What does this show about sound?

Laboratory Exercise—Make a Rubber Band Guitar

Materials
a hammer
2 nails
an assortment of rubber bands
block of wood, at least .6 meter (2 feet) long

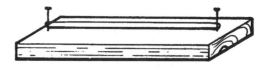
Rubber band guitar

Procedure
Use the hammer and one nail to make a series of holes in which to fit the nails. Space the holes at intervals of 2.5 centimeters (1 inch). Place one nail in the first hole and the second nail far enough along the board to make the rubber band stretch. Place the rubber band over the two nails. (Do not let the rubber band touch the board.) Strum the rubber band and listen to the sound produced. Move the nail farther along the board and strum again. How does the sound change?

Laboratory Exercise—Form a Jug Band

Materials
3 empty 2-liter plastic soda bottles

Jug band

Procedure
1. Leave one bottle empty, fill one bottle halfway, and fill the third bottle to 7.5 centimeters (3 inches) below the top.
2. Practice blowing across the openings of the bottles until you can produce a note. Which bottle produces the highest note? Which produces the lowest note? How can you make the pitch higher or lower? (You can actually make a musical scale by changing the amount of water in each bottle. Ask a music teacher to help you.)

Laboratory Exercise—Calculate the Distance of Lightning

Procedure
You can calculate the approximate distance of a bolt of lightning if you know the speed of sound in air and the time between the flash of lightning and the boom of the thunder. Multiply the time in seconds by the speed of sound in air, which is about about 345 meters (1,132 feet) per second. Your answer will tell how far away the lightning was in meters or feet. To change meters to kilometers, divide by 1,000; to change feet to miles, divide by 5,280.

Lightning

Lenses

Guide Question: What are the two basic kinds of lenses?

Vocabulary: concave focal point magnify
            convex lens refract

A **lens** is a piece of glass or plastic that refracts light. **Refract** means "to bend." You can see light refracted when you look at a straw in a glass of water. The straw looks bent because light travels more slowly through water than it does through air. When rays of light pass through a lens, they are refracted so that they either come together or spread out.

Lenses are useful because they can form images of objects. Images are **magnified,** or made larger, by the lenses of a microscope or telescope. This makes studying small objects, such as living cells, much easier. Lenses are also used in eyeglasses to help people see better.

Most lenses are round, although they could be of any shape. There are two basic types of lenses, concave and convex. **Concave** lenses are "caved in." They are thicker at the edges than in the middle. **Convex** lenses are thicker in the middle than at the edges.

A convex lens converges, or brings together, light rays. The point at which the light rays converge is called the **focal point.** The more curved a convex lens is, the more light it will refract. In a concave lens, the light rays diverge, or spread out, toward the edges of the lens.

In the following experiment, you will study the difference between concave and convex lenses.

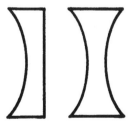

Concave lenses

Convex lens

Laboratory Exercise—Examining Concave and Convex Lenses

Materials
concave lens	convex lens
meter stick or yardstick	candle
2 small balls of clay	index card

Caution: Strike the match carefully, and avoid touching the flame or placing the candle near materials that burn easily.

Procedure

1. Hold the convex lens close to your eye. Observe objects that are far away and some that are close to the lens.
2. Hold the concave lens close to your eye. Observe objects that are far away and some that are close to the lens.
3. Push the edge of the convex lens into a small ball of clay. Push the ball of clay with the lens onto the meter stick 5 centimeters from the end of the stick. (If you are using a yardstick, place it 2 inches from the end.)
4. Push the index card into the other small ball of clay. Push the ball of clay with the index card onto the meter stick.
5. Light the candle and place it on the end of the meter stick nearest the lens.
6. Darken the room as much as possible by turning out the lights and pulling down any shades on the windows.
7. Move the index card back and forth until you see a sharp image of the candle on the card.
8. Repeat the experiment using the concave lens.

■ Interpret the results.

1. Describe how objects look through each of the lenses.

   a. concave lens:_____

   _____

   b. convex lens:_____

   _____

2. Describe the image of the candle that you saw on the index card._____

   _____

3. Were you able to get an image using the concave lens? _____

4. Find someone who is nearsighted and wears glasses. Ask to look through the glasses.

   What kind of lenses do nearsighted people use?_____

Guide Question: What is electricity?

Vocabulary: alternating current (AC)   direct current (DC)   positive charge
  circuit   electric current   static electricity
  current electricity   negative charge

Have you ever walked across a carpet, touched a doorknob, and gotten a shock? Have you rubbed a balloon against a wool sweater and then stuck the balloon to a wall? Rubbing some objects removes electrons and leaves the atoms with more protons than electrons. When the number of protons and electrons are unequal, the atom has a charge.

If an atom has more protons than electrons, it has a **positive charge**. If it has more electrons, it has a **negative charge**. The charges in one substance can build up until they create enough force to cause electrons to transfer to another substance. This transfer produces the spark that occurs between your hand and the doorknob. The transfer of electrons balances the charges in the two substances. The spark is called a discharge. When the charges are balanced, there are an equal number of protons and electrons.

The buildup and discharge of electrons is called **static electricity.** It is the simplest type of electricity. There are many examples of static electricity in nature. The most dramatic example is lightning. Lightning is the result of charges that build up between clouds or between clouds and the surface of the earth. Because static electricity cannot be controlled, it is not useful to people.

Current electricity is electricity that can be controlled, stored, and moved through electric lines. **Electric current** is made either by generators that turn mechanical energy into electric energy or by batteries that turn chemical energy into electric energy.

There are two kinds of electric current. **Direct current,** or **DC,** is the type of electricity that is made by batteries. It is also produced by DC generators. The electrons in DC travel from a negative terminal to a positive terminal. The path the electrons take in going from a negative terminal to a positive terminal is called a **circuit.** By placing an electrical device, such as a light bulb, in the circuit, the electricity can be made to do work.

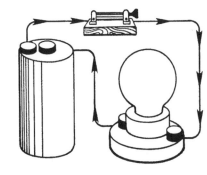

Battery   **Light bulb**

The other form of electric current is called **alternating current,** or **AC.** This type of electric current is produced by generators. In an AC circuit, the electrons rapidly change their direction of movement. This happens because the charge on the terminals switches continually from positive to negative and back.

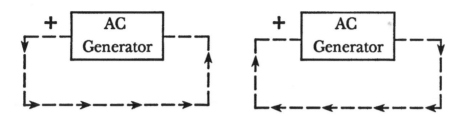

Current flows first in one direction and then in the opposite direction.

Each type of electricity has its advantages and disadvantages. An advantage of direct current is that it is portable. It can be used to power things like radios, flashlights, and toys. Direct current loses a lot of its power if it must travel long distances.

An advantage of alternating current is that it is easily sent over long distances without losing too much power. However, electric appliances that use alternating current must be connected by wire to the generator.

Match the following terms with their meanings.

1. _____ alternating current   **a.** a path for electricity

2. _____ static electricity   **b.** a charge with more electrons than protons

3. _____ circuit   **c.** current flow changes direction rapidly

4. _____ positive   **d.** a charge with more protons than electrons

5. _____ direct current   **e.** the type of electricity in a lightning bolt

6. _____ negative   **f.** current produced by a battery

7. _____ mechanical   **g.** energy used by batteries

8. _____ chemical   **h.** energy used by generators

Batteries and Circuits

Guide Question: How are batteries used in circuits?

Vocabulary:
ampere	negative terminal	positive terminal	volt
circuit	ohm	resistance	voltage
dry-cell battery	parallel circuit	series circuit	wet-cell battery

A battery is a source of electricity that uses chemical reactions to produce charges. A common type of battery is the zinc-carbon type used in flashlights and radios. This type of battery has a **positive terminal** made from a carbon rod. The carbon rod is placed in the center of a zinc can. The zinc can forms the **negative terminal.** The space between the rod and can is filled with a mixture of manganese dioxide and carbon powder. Current is carried within the battery by a paste composed of several chemicals. Batteries in which the current is conducted by a paste or gel are called **dry-cell batteries.**

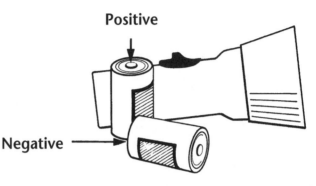

Positive

Negative

Dry-cell battery

Other batteries called **wet-cell batteries** are made from plates of metal covered by a liquid that conducts electricity within the battery. Automobile batteries are wet-cell batteries in which electricity is conducted by sulfuric acid, a highly dangerous acid that can burn the skin. An important advantage of wet-cell batteries is that they can be recharged after they have delivered their electric energy. After recharging, a battery can again produce electric current.

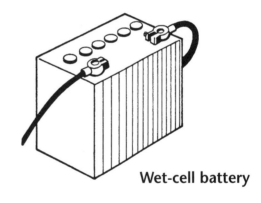

Wet-cell battery

Dry-cell batteries come in many sizes and shapes. The basic zinc-carbon cell has a voltage of 1.5 volts. **Voltage** measures the amount of force or pressure that a battery produces. The voltage is measured in units called **volts.** Cells can be combined in different ways. By combining cells in a **series circuit**, different voltages can be created. For example, a 6-volt battery contains four 1.5-volt cells connected together in series. Cells are in series when the positive terminal of one cell is attached to the negative terminal of another.

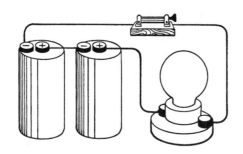

Batteries in series

When cells are connected in series, the total voltage is equal to the sum of the voltages of each cell. The disadvantage of a series circuit is that if there is a break in any part of the circuit, no current can flow. Inexpensive holiday tree lights are often connected in series.

Cells that have the same voltage can also be connected in a **parallel circuit**. This means that the positive terminal of one cell is connected to the positive terminal of another cell. The negative terminals are connected in the same way. The voltage of a parallel circuit is the same as that of each of the individual cells. The amount of electricity that can be used is increased by each cell that is added to the circuit. The amount of electricity flowing through a circuit is measured in *amperes*. If there is a break in a parallel circuit, the current continues to flow through the other branches. Lights and appliances in most houses are connected in parallel circuits.

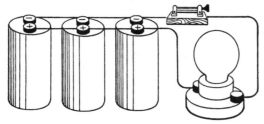

Batteries in parallel

Batteries connected in parallel will last longer than a single cell or cells in series. Dry-cell batteries are available in many different sizes and shapes. The most common sizes are shown to scale below.

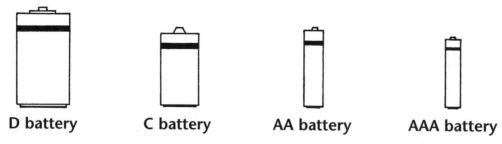

D battery　　　**C battery**　　　**AA battery**　　　**AAA battery**

Electrical circuits are connections that allow the current from a battery to flow through a device that does some type of work. The current flows continually around the circuit from the negative terminal of the battery to the positive terminal.

The devices that are connected to a circuit use up the available electricity. The wire that carries the current uses a small bit of the current to do its work. A device such as a light uses more of the current to do its work. Each part of a circuit has a **resistance** to the force of the current. The current must push harder through a higher resistance. Resistance is measured in **ohms.**

The resistance, current, and voltage in a circuit are related to one another. This relationship can be stated in a formula called Ohm's Law. It allows you to calculate any one of the units when you know the other two. The formula is

I = V ÷ R
current = voltage ÷ resistance

Example 1: How much current flows in a circuit with a battery voltage of 12 volts and a resistance of 6 ohms?

I = V ÷ R
I = 12 volts ÷ 6 ohms
I = 2 amperes

Example 2: How much voltage is needed in a circuit if a light has a resistance of 12 ohms and uses 1 ampere of current?

V = I x R
V = 1 ampere x 12 ohms
V = 12 volts

Example 3: How much resistance does a lamp have if the voltage is 9 volts and the current is .5 amperes?

R = V ÷ I
R = 9 volts ÷ .5 amperes
R = 18 ohms

Solve the following problems using Ohm's Law.

1. How much current flows in a circuit with a battery voltage of 6 volts and a resistance of 2 ohms?

I = V ÷ R   I = _____ volts ÷ _____ ohms   I = _____ amperes

2. How much voltage is needed in a circuit if a light has a resistance of 24 ohms and uses 3 amperes of current?

V = I x R   V = _____ amperes x _____ ohms   V = _____ volts

3. How much resistance does a lamp have if the voltage is 12 volts and the current is 3 amperes?

R = V ÷ I   R = _____ volts ÷ _____ amperes   R = _____ ohms

Laboratory Exercise—Investigating Electric Current

Materials
2 dry-cell batteries (1.5 volts each)   1 battery holder
1 switch   2 sockets for bulbs
2 flashlight bulbs   6 30.5-centimeter (12-inch)
                                                strips of insulated copper wire

Caution: Be sure that the switch is open when you are working on your circuits.

Procedure

1. Construct a circuit using one battery connected to a switch and light as shown below.

2. When you have finished building the circuit, turn the switch on and off. What happens?

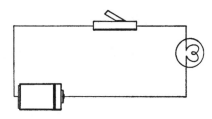

_____

_____

_____

_____

3. Change your circuit to include two batteries connected in a parallel circuit, as shown in the right column.

4. Turn the switch on and off again. Has anything happened to the way the light works? What advantage has been gained by using this circuit?

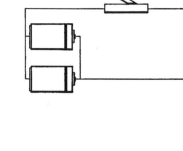

_____

_____

_____

_____

5. Now change your circuit to include two batteries connected in a series circuit as shown in the illustration.
6. Turn the light on and off. What difference is there in the way the light works? Why is this so?

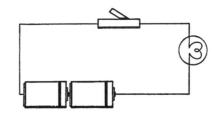

_____
_____
_____
_____
_____

Just as batteries can be connected in series or in parallel circuits, the devices that do work can be connected in series or in parallel circuits. In a series circuit, there is only one path for the electricity to follow. In a series of lights, for example, the current must flow through each bulb.

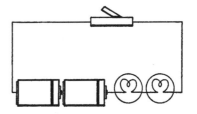

7. Add another light bulb to your circuit as shown in the illustration.
8. Your light bulbs are now connected in a series circuit. Open and close the switch. What happens?

_____
_____
_____
_____

9. Unscrew one of the bulbs. What happens? What is a disadvantage of the series circuit?

_____
_____
_____
_____
_____

In a parallel circuit, the current does not have to flow through each light. There is more than one path for the electricity to follow.

10. Return the bulb to its socket and reconnect the lights in a parallel circuit as shown in the illustration.

11. Unscrew one of the bulbs. What happens? What is an advantage of a parallel circuit?

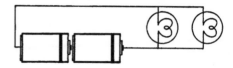

_____

_____

_____

_____

_____

12. Return the bulb to the socket and reconnect the batteries in parallel. What is the advantage of this circuit? What is the disadvantage?

_____

_____

_____

13. Draw a diagram of your circuit in the box below.

Magnetism

Guide Question: What is magnetism?

Vocabulary:
attract   electromagnet   north pole
bar magnet   horseshoe magnet   permanent magnet
circular magnet   lodestone   repel
compass   magnetic field   south pole

A magnet is a piece of metal that attracts other metals. **Lodestone**, a rock made of iron oxide, is a natural magnet. A natural magnet is also a **permanent magnet**, which means that it does not lose its magnetic force.

You have probably played with many different types of permanent magnets. Three common shapes of magnets are the **bar, horseshoe,** and **circular.**

Bar magnet   **Circular magnet**   **Horseshoe magnet**

The atoms that make up a magnet are lined up in such a way that a magnetic field is created. A **magnetic field** is a region of invisible magnetic force that surrounds the magnet. All magnets have a **north pole** and **south pole** where the magnetism is concentrated. (On a circular magnet, the poles are on opposite sides of the disk.)

You can see the effects of a magnetic field and the poles of a magnet by using a bar magnet, iron filings, and a sheet of paper. Place the sheet of paper over the bar magnet and sprinkle some iron filings onto the paper. Tap the paper until the filings line up to show the poles, like this:

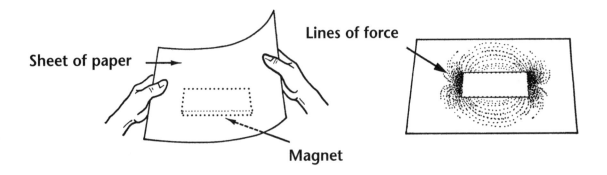

Lines of force

Sheet of paper

Magnet

Because magnets have two poles, they may react in two different ways. Opposite poles will **attract** each other. In other words, a south pole will attract a north pole. Poles that are alike will **repel,** or push away from, each other. A north pole will repel another north pole, and a south pole will repel another south pole.

North and south are opposites.

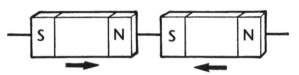

Opposite poles attract.

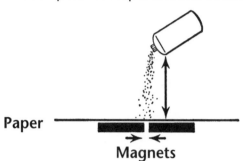

Paper

Magnets

To see this effect more clearly, sprinkle iron filings on a sheet of paper that has been placed over two magnets with the same poles facing each other. The pattern of filings shows the lines of magnetic force. Now clear the sheet and repeat the activity, but with opposite poles facing each other.

The planet Earth is a natural magnet and has magnetic poles just like any other magnet. Earth's magnetic poles are not located at the exact points that we call the North Pole and the South Pole, but they are close to these points.

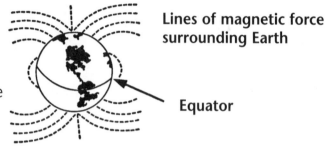

Lines of magnetic force surrounding Earth

Equator

Compass

A **compass** is a small instrument that has a needle that has been magnetized. The needle always lines up with the north-south lines of force in Earth's magnetic field. Because of this property, a compass can be used to identify direction.

If you hold a compass very close to a wire carrying a direct current, the needle will no longer point north. The electric current creates a magnetic field that affects the compass. A compass can be used to show the presence of a current flowing through a wire.

Electricity and magnetism are closely related. Electricity can be used to make a special type of magnet called an electromagnet. **Electromagnets** are made by passing electric current through a wire wrapped around a metal object such as a nail or bolt.

Open switch

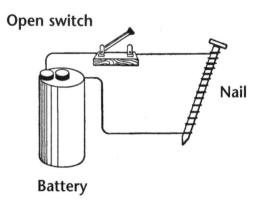

Nail

Battery

Laboratory Exercise—Making an Electromagnet

Materials

copper wire   switch
16-penny nail   paper clips
2 1.5-volt batteries

Caution: Be sure that the switch is open as you build the circuit.

Procedure

1. Make an electromagnet by wrapping 100 turns of copper wire around a 16-penny nail.
2. Connect the ends of the wire to a 1.5-volt battery and a switch as shown in the diagram at the bottom of page 88.
3. Close the switch and test your electromagnet by seeing how many paper clips it will hold at one time. How many paper clips does it hold? What happens when you open the switch?

_____

_____

4. Now change the power source to 3 volts by adding a battery in series with the other battery. How does this affect your electromagnet? Is there a change in the number of paper clips lifted? How many paper clips can now be lifted?

_____

_____

_____

_____

5. Make another electromagnet with 25 turns of wire instead of 100. How does the power of the electromagnet change?

_____

_____

_____

_____

Review Unit 3

A Use each of the following words in the box once to complete the sentences that follow.

speed	accelerate	newton	kinetic
potential	work	reaction	lever
calorie	ohm	force	poles

1. Average _____ is the distance traveled divided by the time taken.

2. To _____ means to increase speed.

3. A _____ is a push or a pull.

4. A _____ is the metric unit of force.

5. For every action, there is an equal and opposite _____.

6. _____ energy is energy in action.

7. _____ energy is stored energy.

8. When a force moves an object, we can say that _____ has been done.

9. A _____ is a bar that is free to rotate around a fulcrum.

10. A _____ is a unit of heat energy.

11. The _____ is a measure of resistance.

12. Magnets have _____ where magnetism is concentrated.

B Solve each of the problems.

1. A cyclist rode for 5 hours and at an average speed of 8 miles per hour. What was the distance the cyclist covered during the ride?

   d = s x t _____ miles

2. A car is traveling at 55 kilometers per hour. This speed is increased to 75 kilometers per hour. If the time needed to change speed is 4 seconds, what is the acceleration?

   a = s ÷ t _____ kph/sec

3. If an object has a mass of 10 kilograms and is pushed by a force of 50 newtons, what will the acceleration be?

   a = f ÷ m _____ meters/sec/sec

4. How much current flows in a circuit with a battery voltage of 48 volts and a resistance of 8 ohms?

   I = V ÷ R _____ amperes

C Unscramble each of the following groups of letters to answer each question.

1. The three methods by which heat travels are _____ dratiiona
   _____ tiocudnocn   _____ vonectoinc

2. Three types of simple machines are _____ elpuyl
   _____ dencilin nelpa   _____ gedew

D Underline the word that does not belong in each of the following groups.

1. Sound: hertz   frequency   amperes
2. Light: color   pitch   reflection
3. Electricity: lens   ohms   amps
4. Magnetism: pole   frequency   repel
5. Heat: degree   fulcrum   calorie

E Read an article about a subject in physical science on the Internet or in a magazine. Use the lines below to help prepare a report on the article. Then write the report on a separate sheet of paper. Your teacher may want you to present your report to the class.

Title of article: _____

Author: _____

Title of publication: _____

Issue and/or date of publication: _____

Topic from this text that article is about: _____

Page number(s): _____

Main idea(s):

_____

_____

F List five questions that can be answered by reading this article.

1. _____

2. _____

3. _____

4. _____

5. _____

End-of-Book Test

A Write the word or phrase from the box that is being defined. You will not use all the words and phrases.

decibel	joule	simple machine	work	accelerate
volume	sound wave	acoustics	ohm	repel
vibrate	convex lens	mixture	proton	litmus paper
atom	solution	atomic number	element	sound wave
neutron	property	compound	nucleus	concave lens

_____ 1. mixture in which one substance is dissolved in another

_____ 2. characteristic of a substance

_____ 3. number of protons in the nucleus of an atom

_____ 4. amount of space an object takes up

_____ 5. building block of matter

_____ 6. simplest type of pure substance

_____ 7. two or more elements chemically combined

_____ 8. center of an atom

_____ 9. two or more substances mixed but not chemically combined

_____ 10. positively charged particle in the nucleus of an atom

_____ 11. to increase in speed

_____ 12. force moving an object

_____ 13. metric unit of work

_____ 14. device that can improve the ability to do work

_____ 15. to move back and forth

_____ 16. science of sound

_____ 17. measurement of the intensity of sound

_____ 18. lens that is thicker at the ends than in the middle

_____ 19. measurement of resistance

_____ 20. to push away from

B Write *True* if the statement is true. Write *False* if the statement is not true.

_____ 1. New ideas scientists have about how the physical world operates are called laws.

_____ 2. In science, the metric system is usually used to record measurement.

_____ 3. Degrees Fahrenheit is the only measure for temperature.

_____ 4. Graphs are a way to organize and summarize information.

_____ 5. Atoms can be seen with a very powerful electron microscope.

_____ 6. Only compounds contain atoms; mixtures do not.

_____ 7. Each element has several symbols that can be used to identify it.

_____ 8. An acid will turn litmus paper bright blue.

_____ 9. Because many substances dissolve in water, it is sometimes called the universal solvent.

_____ 10. In a suspension, some substances do not dissolve in a liquid.

_____ 11. Some mixtures can be separated into their parts by evaporating the water found in them.

_____ 12. Lemonade and vinegar are examples of bases.

_____ 13. A graduated cylinder can be used to measure the volume of a liquid.

_____ 14. A barometer is a scientific instrument used to measure air pressure.

_____ 15. One kilogram is equal to one hundred grams.

_____ 16. A force that operates everywhere on Earth is gravity.

_____ 17. In the metric system, force is measured in newtons.

_____ 18. According to Newton's Third Law of Motion, every action has a reaction.

_____ 19. Stored energy is also known as potential energy.

_____ 20. Joules are measured in foot-pounds.

_____ 21. There are three types of simple machines.

_____ 22. A simple machine can change the direction of an applied force.

_____ 23. Warm air rises, and cold air falls.

_____ 24. Lightning is an example of static electricity.

_____ 25. Because static electricity cannot be controlled, it has no value to people.

_____ 26. In a parallel circuit, all the lights will go out if one light does.

_____ 27. Wet-cell batteries are commonly used in portable CD players.

_____ 28. In magnets, opposite poles attract each other.

_____ 29. A lodestone is a natural magnet.

_____ 30. A compass has a magnetized needle.

C Write the name of the element represented by each symbol. Refer to the list on page 33 if you need help.

1. C _____

2. Zn _____

3. Na _____

4. K _____

5. Au _____

6. Fe _____

7. S _____

8. Rn _____

9. O _____

10. H _____

11. Pb _____

12. Al _____

D Underline the word that correctly completes each sentence.

1. The study of motion and force is called (chemistry, physics, biology).

2. In science, the (metric, English, basic) system of measurement is usually used.

3. The amount of space that an object takes up is its (shape, volume, proportion).

4. A (bar, line, pie) graph has a circular shape.

5. Each element has a (formula, table, symbol), which is an abbreviation for its name.

6. One property of matter is (density, chemical, electricity).

7. A chemical formula is a little like a (magnet, recipe, property).

8. For work to be done, an object must (pay, explode, move).

E Find the words or phrases that go with each heading. Write the words or phrases under the heading.

battery	lever
screw	volt
pulley	circuit

Simple machines

1. _____

2. _____

3. _____

Electricity

4. _____

5. _____

6. _____

bitter	sour
contain OH radical	contain hydrogen
low pH	high pH

Acids

7. _____

8. _____

9. _____

Bases

10. _____

11. _____

12. _____

conduction	vibration
convection	intensity
frequency	calorie

Heat

13. _____

14. _____

15. _____

Sound

16. _____

17. _____

18. _____

TEST

F Write a brief answer to each question.

1. What is the difference between an electron and a proton?

_____

_____

2. What is the difference between a compound and a mixture?

_____

_____

3. What are five properties of an element?

_____

_____

4. What is the difference between potential energy and kinetic energy?

_____

_____

5. What is the difference between alternating current (AC) and direct current (DC)?

_____

_____

6. What is the difference between an element and a compound?

_____

_____

7. What advantage does a wet-cell batter have over a dry-cell battery?

_____

_____